Romance ®

"FACE IT, ZACHARY. IT'S BEEN WONDERFUL, BUT IT'S OVER."

"It's still the same problem, isn't it? You still think I'll regret marrying you because you can't have children. You're doing this out of some crazy belief that you're saving me from myself."

In a way he was right, but he'd reasoned backward. She wasn't going to trap him with a child he didn't want. "Zachary, accept it. I don't want to see you anymore. Children have nothing to do with it."

"Bull!" He walked over and sat beside her. "What else can I say? I don't want children, Rachel, I want you—only you. I'm too selfish to be a father."

Tears started forming in Rachel's eyes. With every word he cut her a little more, tore at her heart a little harder. "Stop it! Stop!"

"I'll never change my mind, Rachel, never. I hate children. Always underfoot, in the way. I—"

With a heart-rending sob Rachel tore herself away from him. She'd been right, so right. "I hate you!" she cried, opening the door with a jerk. "Get out!"

A CANDLELIGHT ECSTASY ROMANCE ®

The Best Things in Life

Linda Vail

A CANDLELIGHT ECSTASY ROMANCE ®

Published by
Dell Publishing Co., Inc.
1 Dag Hammarskjold Plaza
New York, New York 10017

ISBN: 0-440-10494-7

Printed in the United States of America
First printing—June 1984

To Our Readers:

We have been delighted with your enthusiastic response to Candlelight Ecstasy Romances®, and we thank you for the interest you have shown in this exciting series.

In the upcoming months we will continue to present the distinctive sensuous love stories you have come to expect only from Ecstasy. We look forward to bringing you many more books from your favorite authors and also the very finest work from new authors of contemporary romantic fiction.

As always, we are striving to present the unique, absorbing love stories that you enjoy most—books that are more than ordinary romance.

Your suggestions and comments are always welcome. Please write to us at the address below.

Sincerely,

The Editors
Candlelight Romances
1 Dag Hammarskjold Plaza
New York, New York 10017

CHAPTER ONE

"That Lyons character is here again, Rachel," her secretary's voice told her quietly over the intercom. "This time he's really steamed. Wants to talk to you personally."

Rachel Jordan sighed. The healthy tan of her recent vacation in Hawaii was still glowing. Beautiful pale streaks in her shoulder-length dark brown hair gave testimony to her two weeks in the sun, and on her first day back this had to happen.

It had been a relaxing, well-deserved break, and her mind replayed the glorious sound of the surf and laughter on the beach. She could almost hear the soft tinkle of ice in a cold rum drink, feel the chill of the glass as she lazily smoothed its cooling surface across her sun-warmed skin. Rachel was thirty-five, but her supple form, firm curves, and carefree attitude often led people to assume she was much younger. Far from hiding behind her youthful looks, she took delight in revealing her true age—she was proud she'd kept herself in shape and equally proud of the position in life her years had gotten her.

She blinked and was back in her richly paneled office, back behind her massive oak desk, back in charge of Jordan Motorcars. Not that it was a tedious job by any means. In five short years she, and a handful of like-minded individuals, had built a reputation as one of the finest sales and service facilities for antique and classic automobiles in Texas. Born of a long-standing love affair with the graceful lines and subdued grace of the very best the world's car makers had to offer, a dream had come true. In fact, the dream was still growing, ready to expand from the already too small showroom and service shop.

With this and other problems to contend with, the last thing Rachel needed was some impossibly obnoxious patron. A patron, she thought with disdain, who had single-handedly managed to turn her efficient staff upside down in the two brief weeks she'd been gone. "So be it." She sighed. With one last thought of distant beaches, Rachel pushed the button on her intercom.

"Send the gentleman in, Angela."

She had been prepared for this meeting by her staff and was used to dealing with finicky owners who treated their cars like pets or even like pampered children. But none of her considerable experience had prepared her for the man who walked through her office door.

Tall and lean, dressed impeccably in a three-piece gray suit, Mr. Lyons entered her office with all the dignity and grace of a jungle cat. Rachel's gaze was instantly drawn to his eyes, as coal black as his hair and shining with an inner intensity that was at once engaging and intimidating. He seemed, in a way, like one of the cars on her showroom floor, fast and sleek, with terrifying power cloaked beneath a velvety smooth exterior. His jaw was strong, his cheekbones were prominent, and his nose could only be described as aristocratic. He looked to be in his early forties and radiated vitality. Rachel, though hardly prone to such things, felt an instant and nearly electric attraction to him.

By the way his eyes raked over her and the barely perceptible smile that tugged at one corner of his sensuous mouth, Rachel knew instinctively the feeling was mutual. His strong, sinewy grip lingered a moment longer than necessary when he shook her hand, and she glanced down, noticing that her tanned skin seemed pale next to his. "Zachary Lyons," he said in a voice Rachel felt as well as heard.

"Rachel Jordan. Please have a seat, Mr. Lyons," she replied when he at last let go of her hand.

He seemed to study her emerald-colored eyes

closely as he sat down and carelessly crossed his legs. "I'm honored. It seems you're a very difficult person to see," he stated crisply.

"I assure you, Mr. Lyons, I wasn't giving you the runaround. I've been in Hawaii for the past two weeks," she explained.

"I see. Business or pleasure?"

His tone was conversational now, and Rachel made a mental note that this man's mercurial shifts in attitude could be dangerous. She knew she'd have to concentrate fully on what he was saying. Not an easy task, considering how striking he was. No wonder Angela had been flustered just talking about him. "Pleasure. I lay around in the sun for the most part."

Again he stared at her intensely, his gaze lingering pointedly at the open V of her cream blouse as if verifying her words by her tanned skin. "That must have been very pleasant. Especially for your companion."

His dark gaze flicked back to her eyes, leaving no doubt in her mind what he meant. "I went alone," she returned coolly. Whatever his tactics were, she wasn't about to let him get the upper hand in this conversation. "I understand you've had a few minor problems with your Duesenberg."

His black eyes narrowed dangerously in another abrupt shift of temperament. "They weren't few, and they weren't minor."

"I know the history of the car and the circumstances of its purchase, Mr. Lyons. You were informed it wasn't in excellent shape, that it needed some work and final restoration," she pointed out, trying to remain civil. She didn't like the tone of his voice or the implications of his statement.

"Granted. I'm not saying you didn't warn me. What galls me is the trouble I've had getting those problems corrected."

He didn't need to elaborate to get his point across. She already had her best mechanic threatening to attack the man on sight. "We have a busy shop, Mr. Lyons. We need more space and more staff. Unfortunately, for now, our customers have to cooperate with us. Most do so gladly."

Zachary Lyons's eyebrows arched at the ring of pride in her words. "You're taking this personally, aren't you?" he asked with surprise.

"When you insult my company or my staff, you are insulting me as well." Rachel tried to ease the tension out of her voice, not quite successfully.

He leaned forward slightly, his expression masked. "Tell me, Rachel, do I look crazy to you?"

This time his changing manner caught her off guard. She met his intense gaze uncertainly. "What?"

"I'd have to be crazy to insult a beautiful woman like you purposely, especially before we've even gotten to know each other."

Rachel uttered a short, incredulous laugh.

"You may not be crazy, Mr. Lyons, but you have to be one of the most unusual men I've ever met. I thought we were talking about your Duesenberg."

"Oh, that," he replied, waving his hand in dismissal.

She looked at him skeptically. "You harass my staff for two weeks, then suddenly drop it as if it didn't matter anymore?"

"I've found something much more interesting to divert my attention," he said, his eyes taking on another kind of gleam. He smiled, revealing even white teeth. His gaze was so direct as he looked into Rachel's eyes that she almost felt as if he had touched her. It was not an altogether unpleasant feeling.

There was no doubt in her mind what had become the object of his attention. Still, she found herself asking, "What do you mean?"

"Have dinner with me this evening, and I'll show you."

Rachel's eyes widened. Perhaps she had been wrong. Perhaps he was crazy. "Ridiculous."

"Why?"

"Mr. Lyons—"

"Zachary," he interrupted her to say.

"I'm a busy woman, Zachary, and this conversation isn't getting us anywhere," she continued, anger creeping into her tone. "Although I sometimes socialize with people I do business with, they are usually people I know, people with interests similar to mine. I don't think you qualify."

His eyes narrowed slightly at her remark. "Meaning?"

Rachel sighed. "Look, Mr.—Zachary, I think we've gotten off to a bad start here. Put the blame on me if you like; this is my first day back, and perhaps I haven't settled down yet. Let's confine ourselves to your—"

Zachary leaned across her desk with a fluid motion and casually reached out to put a finger under her chin. "What kind of people do you deign to associate with, Miss Jordan?" he asked, his eyes locked to hers.

Startled by his unexpected contact, Rachel jerked her head away from his touch, her pulse leaping. "Mr. Lyons," she said in a dangerously soft voice, "I have a chief mechanic just a stone's throw away who would simply love to use his skill at taking things apart on you. Shall I call him?" Her finger hovered over the buttons of her intercom.

The big man grinned with maddening self-assurance. "That might be interesting. I suppose an establishment such as this has a couple of guys named Louie with broken noses and violin cases. They'd go well with the gangster-type cars." He casually leaned back in the chair. "Do you want to scream for them, too?"

"What is it you want from me?"

"Oh, I can think of quite a few things," he replied sardonically. "But for starters, I'd like an

15

answer to my question. I've been around enough to recognize that special spark of interest in a woman's eyes when she looks at a man she finds attractive. Why are you trying to convince me I'm not your type?"

She folded her hands on top of her desk and fixed him with a steady gaze. "It has been my experience that people who buy Duesenbergs do so mainly—if not entirely—for investment purposes. They keep them in specially built garages with central heat and air conditioning, tote them around the country to inflate their prices with show ribbons, and rarely, if ever, drive them."

"So? It's their money and their cars. And," he continued, looking at her directly, "you're still avoiding my question, Rachel."

"No, I'm not. I am deliberately choosing not to answer you," she retorted sharply. "We're here to discuss your problems with my company, not whether you're my type."

His smile was warm and friendly. "Your voice is as beautiful as you are, Rachel. And I like the fire in your eyes when you're angry."

This conversation was getting out of hand. "I see my staff was right. You are obnoxious, insulting, and rude."

"And I think you're very sexy, Rachel."

Rachel opened her mouth to speak, but her intercom began to buzz. It was a lucky event because she really didn't know what to say to his outrageous comment. "Yes, Angela?"

16

"Rachel, I think you'd better come out here. A truck just pulled up, and, well, you'd just better see what they put in the driveway."

No sooner had Angela spoken than Zachary jumped up, a stricken look on his face. "Oh, God! No!"

"What on earth—"

He turned to her, his face visibly pale beneath his tan. "Rachel, please don't go out there. Don't walk out that door!"

She frowned at him in confusion, her wariness suddenly mounting. "Why not?"

"Let me take care of it. It's just something I—I mean, I didn't know you—" he sputtered helplessly as he watched her walk out of the office.

Rachel looked through the plate-glass window to where Angela was pointing. There, in the middle of the parking area in front of the building, was a large, rectangular block of crumpled metal. She knew what it was immediately, having seen enough of them in junkyards. And if she had any doubts what kind of car the block had once been, they were banished by the horror-stricken expression of the tall man standing beside her and the distinctive Duesenberg hood ornament sticking out of the top of the block.

She stood there for a moment, blinking at the bright sunlight glinting on shining steel, then turned slowly to face Zachary. "You had it crushed," she said, the disbelief plain in her low voice.

"Let me explain—"

"No!" She shoved past him, trying to escape his presence.

He followed her doggedly. "It's not what you think."

She turned on him furiously. "It's obvious to me now you don't give a damn about what I think. Get the hell out of my shop before I call the police," she said vehemently.

"The police? What for?"

"For . . . for littering!"

"If you'll only listen to reason for a minute—"

She looked over his shoulder, a grim smile forming on her face. "I don't think you have that long, Mr. Lyons."

He turned and saw about a dozen angry mechanics crossing the parking lot, some carrying heavy instruments. He turned back to her, and she saw with amazement that no trace of worry or fear showed on his face. "Discretion being the better part of valor, I think I'll take my leave now. But you haven't heard the last of this," he declared, and headed for a door in the opposite direction from the approaching mob.

Fighting to maintain some sense of order, Rachel called out to him as he opened the door. "You're damn right this isn't over! You still owe on that car!"

Zachary Lyons turned before he walked out. "The check, Miss Jordan, is in the glove compartment." He pointed to the crushed metal block, smiled winningly, then left at a sedate and dignified pace.

CHAPTER TWO

"This is terrible!" Rachel cried. "Just too horrible to be true!" A feeling of impending doom settled over her, and she fought the impulse to tear the sheet of paper she was holding into little bits.

The week had started badly anyway. First there had been the impudent Zachary Lyons, awakening in her a turmoil she could easily do without. During the course of their brief conversation Rachel had gone from instant attraction to wary consternation. Then he had committed an act of unspeakable barbarity that still made her tremble with anger when she thought of it.

It was now Thursday, and an air of bereavement lingered over Jordan Motorcars, brought on by the forlorn block of metal sitting in the

19

corner of the service building. Classic car people in general, and Rachel's staff in particular, were a bit fanatic about the old vehicles; many thought of them as their children. Several times she had thought she would physically have to restrain Martin, her chief mechanic, from seeking reprisals against Zachary.

Now, with the information she held on the slip of paper in front of her, her entire world had turned upside down. "There couldn't have been a mistake, I suppose?" she asked the silver-haired, somewhat paunchy real estate agent who sat before her.

"No, ma'am. It's all a matter of public record. The owner of that land is Mr. Zachary Lyons," he drawled.

Rachel, though not particularly fond of the man, had no reason to doubt him. They had done business before, and she had found him to be honest and trustworthy. "This just can't be happening to me," she wailed in disbelief.

The agent proceeded to tell her what she already knew. Undeveloped land in Houston wasn't just scarce, but at a premium. That she was terribly lucky to have such a parcel adjacent to her own property went without saying. Add the undeniable need for that land to expand her burgeoning business, and you had what could only be called an extremely happy circumstance. Happy that is, except for the man she would have to deal with to get that land.

Rachel thanked the agent and assured him

that although she herself might be in contact with Mr. Lyons, she would still call upon him to complete any transactions and he would receive his full commission on any sale that resulted. Though she had the knowledge and business acumen to buy or sell her own house, commercial property was another matter.

Angela later brought in coffee and sympathy. "This is one of the few times I don't envy your position, Rachel. I can only imagine what it will be like to have to butter that guy up."

"I don't intend to butter him up, Angela," she told the petite blue-eyed blonde. "It's just a business transaction."

"Sure it is," the younger woman replied skeptically. "I saw the way he looked at you."

Rachel could hardly overlook the sparkle in her secretary's eyes. "It's true I'll have to get on better terms with him before I ask him about the land. He'll be in a good enough position to gouge me as it is without there being any animosity between us. But doing my best to forget the incident with his Duesenberg is as far as I plan to go on that score, I assure you."

"Um-hmm," Angela murmured doubtfully. "He's one hunk of a good-looking male Rachel, and it's obvious he's interested in you. If I were you, I'd be worried he might require some rather unusual concessions in return for a fair price on his property."

"Angela!"

She smiled. "I will now take my overly large nose and return it to the grindstone."

"Good idea," Rachel retorted with friendly severity. Angela hadn't said a thing she wasn't already turning around in her own mind. When Zachary told her she hadn't heard the last of him, she knew he wasn't referring to their business dealings. She tried to convince herself that all she felt toward him was anger, but she knew her argument didn't hold water. Zachary was right; she recognized the sparks of sexual interest when she felt them. A smile traced itself upon her full lips. It was a shame Mr. Zachary Lyons had turned out to be so obnoxious. Rachel pushed some rather disturbing images from her mind and returned to the business at hand.

It would be necessary to keep her true intentions from Zachary for a while, at least until she had a better idea of who and what he was. Building a little goodwill before negotiations started seemed the thing to do, if only to gain some small advantage in what could be a tricky bit of financing. Not to mention the fact that if she didn't put their differences behind them, he could very well refuse to sell or put the price out of reach. No, it would be better all around if she could forge some kind of friendship before telling him she needed his land. If she worked everything just right, she thought, it would seem like a natural turn of events to Zachary.

Accustomed to such social politics, Rachel knew just how to proceed. She needed an initial contact point, and by Friday afternoon she had settled on one. "Mr. Lyons?" she said over the phone in a businesslike voice. It wouldn't do to arouse suspicions by acting too friendly considering the way their last meeting had gone.

"Miss Jordan?" Zachary's deep, smooth voice sounded wary and surprised. "Calling to apologize?"

Apologize! Rachel nearly bit her tongue to prevent herself from screaming at him. It wasn't going to be easy to calm herself, but she would have to because she was now doubly worried. The number she had dialed to reach him was listed as Lyons Construction. He could easily already have plans for the land she wanted. "Actually, I called to see if we could get together about payment for your late, lamented Duesenberg," she replied, chuckling convincingly even though her heart wasn't in it.

There was a long silence over the line, and Rachel held her breath, hoping she hadn't already managed to mess things up. His voice, when it finally came, was friendly enough but oddly strained. "I take it you haven't tried to retrieve my check."

"Come now, Zachary," she replied, "you know as well as I how difficult that would be." Actually she hadn't had the heart to heap any more indignities on the remains of the once-proud vehicle. "I was hoping to convince you to cancel that check and write us a new one."

"I will, on one condition. Have dinner with

23

me this evening." This time his tone sounded sincere.

Rachel breathed a sigh of relief. If he hadn't asked her, she had planned to ask him. Had she imagined it, or was there even a trace of warmth in his voice? "Well, let me check my calendar." She covered the receiver with her hand for a moment, grinning mischievously. "This evening would be fine. Shall we say around seven?"

"Just a second, let me check my calendar," he replied. She could hear the laughter in his voice. "Seven is fine. Where shall I pick you up?" She gave him directions to her home, and they said good-bye.

Rachel wore a simple bone-colored sheath and high-heeled sandals that emphasized her firm calves and long legs. When she met Zachary at her door, he seemed even more handsome than she remembered. His boots were round-toed, of a natural tan leather that went well with his camel-colored slacks and sports coat. A cream-colored shirt, open at the neck, revealed tanned skin and curly black hair that almost matched his eyes exactly. Amusement seemed to lurk in their depths as he slowly looked her over. "Do I pass inspection?" she asked, feeling a disconcerting rush of excitement at seeing him again.

"Yes. Very much so." His dark eyes roamed over her.

When they walked into the restaurant, Rachel

was acutely aware of the glances in their direction. She herself was tall but Zachary was well over six feet, his well-muscled frame carrying the height well. She couldn't mistake the interested looks he received from the other women diners.

They ordered the fine Gulf seafood that was the restaurant's specialty and a dry white wine. As they ate, they talked leisurely while watching the night traffic on Houston's Ship Channel. The lights of the ferry below them glimmered across the water. A light fog was drifting in, making the whole scene seem mysterious and exotic. It reminded Rachel that Zachary himself was something of an enigma to her. It was time for her to find out more about him. "So," Rachel asked, fixing him with an inquiring gaze, "just what is your business, Zachary?" Far from being on pins and needles as she'd feared, she was truly enjoying herself.

Zachary, his eyes glowing with an inner warmth, replied, "You mean Lyons Construction? That's only one aspect of my company. We have our corporate finger in many different pies these days. We started out building roads for oil drilling crews, then slowly got into oil leases and branched out from there. I have spent my fair share of time behind a shovel, though."

"You appear to be in pretty good shape," she said, eyeing him speculatively. "I'd say it wasn't that long ago."

"I take care of myself," he said, pleased that

she had noticed. Now to return the compliment. His eyes roved over her appraisingly. "It's obvious you do, too," he said appreciatively.

"Thank you. I do work at it." Oh, how she worked at it!

"That's what it takes," he said in agreement. He smiled, took a sip of wine, then asked. "Do you exercise at a health club?"

"As often as I can," she replied. "The club I belong to is pretty busy. Occasionally I can't afford the time."

"We could have a workout at my home sometime," he said, then paused, pleased by her startled reaction. He continued, "I have a complete gym in my home. Swimming pool, sauna, weight machine . . ."

"Oh. Well . . ." Rachel didn't believe for a minute that exercise in his gym was the only exercise he had in mind. But a private gym was almost too good an opportunity to miss. No standing in line for machines or swimming lanes. She could also use this as an opportunity to further their business relationship. Still . . . "I like the supervised environment at my club . . ." she began.

"Yes, but think about having the sauna to yourself—almost," he said coaxingly.

That did sound nice. It was as if he had read her mind. But the "almost" bothered her. "We'll see."

Zachary nodded. "How about you? How is it you came to head such an unusual enterprise?"

Rachel breathed a sigh of relief at the change of subject. "I think it was probably inevitable, although I've been very lucky, if you could call it that," she replied wryly.

"How so?"

"I started out just interested in business. Degree in business administration and all that, but all the while I had this intense interest in automobiles—old ones, new ones, anything with wheels and an engine."

"Unusual interest for a—"

"Woman?" she interrupted him to say.

He grinned. "I was going to say for a business major."

"Sure you were." Rachel laughed. "Either way you're right, I suppose. But it did get me a job with one of the big three automakers. Which one I refuse to divulge."

"That bad?"

"Terrible." She looked up uncertainly. "It was there I met my ex-husband." He looked unconcerned by her statement, so she continued. "We had as many problems with our marriage as I did with my job, so . . ."

"So you opened up your own car company."

"Not directly no. I had acquired an elderly British car, which I sold after the divorce for about three times its original cost. That was the beginning of an idea. I handled some similar sales for friends, with the same good fortune, then got a small place and started selling antique and classic cars on consignment. With the help of some investors I moved to the present location, doing much the same thing. I eventually gathered enough capital to start hitting the car auctions to build an inventory of my own. Then one thing followed another, and here I am," she finished.

"And now you're surrounded by them. You sell them, buy them, service and restore them. No wonder you have that air of accomplishment."

"That's why I said it was inevitable. I had my sights set high, and I think in order to succeed in business, you have to like the business you're in. I love classic cars."

"So what are you doing having dinner and a pleasant conversation with a man who squashed one?" he asked intently.

Though she knew he would ask this question sometime and though she was prepared for it, his manner of injecting it midstream like this took her by surprise. She was sure that had been his intention. She stared at him blankly, waiting for him to continue.

"You know my credit rating, so I'm sure you're not worried about getting your money. And however much I'd like to believe you've been overwhelmed by my manly charms, you strike me as a lady who has her emotions pretty well in control."

He didn't know just how close he was to being wrong about that, she thought. "After studying the matter fully, I've calmed down quite a bit," she replied honestly. "First of all, what's done is done. No amount of retribution will change that."

Zachary was watching her face closely. "And second?"

"I think you might have acquired that rarest of the rare—a classic lemon. I was prepared to buy the car back from you as a matter of fact."

"Now she tells me." He chuckled.

"While I don't condone the kind of drastic action you took, I would like to know what drove you to it."

Zachary smiled mysteriously. "You'll find out . . . eventually."

"Why not now?" she asked in irritation.

"Because I'm not ready to let you know yet," he answered simply.

Before she could object, he signaled the waitress and paid their bill. "Now, how would you like to get a look at a vintage Jaguar sedan—and my home?"

"Why should I go anywhere with you? Especially your home?" she demanded sharply.

"If you don't, you may never find out what drove me to take such drastic action, or see my sauna or . . . my vintage Jaguar," he finished, his eyes laughing wickedly.

As irritating as he was, Zachary obviously knew the way to her heart. "That's an unusual line to use to get a woman to come home with you," she replied, amusement dancing in her green eyes.

"You're an unusual woman. Besides, it's better than asking you to look at my etchings. The question is: Did it work?"

He made the word "unusual" sound like a compliment. "Perfectly. I'd rather look at an engine than an etching any day."

Zachary lived in a sprawling, ranch-style house in the middle of several acres on the outskirts of Houston. The peace and quiet were a welcome change from Rachel's uptown apartment. "Are those stables?" she asked, pointing to the long building off to one side of the house.

"Used to be. I converted them into garage stalls," he explained, helping her out of his car. The touch of his strong, sinewy hand was warm. She hadn't forgotten what he had said about being aware of her attraction to him. That attraction, temporarily smoldering after their first meeting, was coming back full strength now as she walked beside him to the garage. His aftershave didn't overpower the clean male scent of his skin in the misty night air. It was the kind of evening that reminded Rachel of tropical islands, spicy trade winds, and pagan passions. She needed no reminder of the rapid increase in her heartbeat when Zachary looked at her, though, and her skin was warm with more than just the evening's heat.

"I hope you'll forgive me, Rachel," Zachary commented, remembering her distaste for owners who pampered their cars. "But the garage does have air conditioning. It's not for the cars, though; it's for me when I work out here."

She instantly forgave him when she stepped into the darkened interior of the building, reveling in the cool air. It helped give her a better perspective on who she was with and why she was here. Then the lights switched on overhead, and she suddenly had other things to think about.

Before her sat a gleaming MGTD, one of the finest examples of the British automaker's art, its chrome, brass, and dark green paint as shiny as the day it had rolled out of the factory more than thirty years ago. The smell of rich leather upholstery enticed her closer, and she ran her hand over the sports car's sweeping lines. "You've taken very good care of it, Zachary," she said as she looked it over with an expert eye. "It runs, I assume."

"Like a top. I'll take you for a ride in it someday soon."

"I'd enjoy that." Actually she would enjoy any situation that would bring her close to him. Her opinion of Zachary was improving by the minute. When she saw his other car, a beautiful, elegant Jaguar sedan, and his complete stock of tools, she began to understand much more about him as well. "You're a do-it-yourselfer, aren't you?"

He smiled and nodded. "That, Rachel, is my passion. Restoring these lovely machines myself." He moved closer to her, and even in the cool air of the garage she could feel the heat of his body. "Or *one* of my passions," he said seductively.

Zachary pulled her gently against him, his lips brushing intimately over hers. At first she resisted; but slowly his soft, sensuous kiss ignited a spark within her, and she parted her lips, allowing full access to the hot cavern of her mouth. His tongue slowly circled her lips, then plunged deeply between them, exploring her offering fully. His hands ran smoothly over her back and pressed her against his full, hard length, leaving her with no doubts about the state of his arousal.

When their lips finally parted, Rachel's breath was ragged and hard to control. Zachary looked searchingly into her eyes, their emerald depths revealing her flaming desire. "Why don't we go inside and have some vintage wine to go with the vintage cars?"

Never had Rachel felt such an intense longing to be with a man. Not even her ex-husband had set off the kind of fireworks in her that Zachary had. He wrapped his arm loosely around her waist as they walked back to his house, and she felt as if it belonged right where it was.

Zachary led her through the front door and down a short hallway to a masculinely furnished den. The leather upholstery felt cool against her skin when she sat on the couch while he went to get the wine. Her every sense seemed alive to her surroundings. Colorful paintings of antique racing cars were hung on the walls. A large saltwater aquarium, set into the wall in front of her, bubbled softly, its tropical occupants swimming and darting unconcernedly in their watery home.

"Here we are," Zachary said as he sat down beside her and offered her a glass of deeply colored Burgundy.

Rachel sipped her wine and gazed tranquilly at the aquarium. "You lead a nice life, Zachary," she murmured.

"I've been lucky." He shrugged.

Rachel shook her head. "I doubt luck had much to do with it. You seem the kind of man who wouldn't settle for anything less." She looked at him and felt another pang of longing deep within her. Zachary Lyons was quite a man: confident and self-assured, comfortable with his surroundings, undeniably handsome, sexy. "I find it strange you don't have a woman sharing all this with you."

"I've been around enough to know what I want," he replied casually. "And I generally get what I go after."

The look in his eyes told her that what he wanted now was herself. The knowledge caused a delicious tightening in the muscles of her stomach. "I'm sure you do."

"I find it strange that a beautiful and intelligent woman like you hasn't been snatched up before now."

"I was once, remember?"

"He was a fool to let you go," Zachary replied softly.

Rachel's mind returned to her marriage and her divorce. Fresh out of college, eager and full of life, Rachel gratefully accepted the help she received in landing her first job. The helping hand was attached to an enticingly powerful man named Bill Myler, and after a brief courtship they were married. At first it was a dream come true: a good job, or at least a good-paying one; a fine home; and an attentive, if somewhat overly assertive, husband. Wasn't that what she had been led to believe life was about?

Then things changed. At first gradually, then with alarming swiftness, the shortcomings in her life were made plain to her. She wasn't particularly ecstatic about her job, but she loved to work and gave it everything she had. Bill wanted children, and she agreed, thinking it would bring them closer together. Rachel had felt perfectly capable of handling both career and motherhood, but Bill wasn't even willing to let her try. He wanted his wife at home, rearing the kids—preferably boys to carry on the family name.

Try as they might, however, Rachel couldn't get pregnant. Bill blamed her long hours and ordered her to quit her job; to quiet his tyrannical ravings, she did so. Still no pregnancy. Their sex life became a depressingly mechanical series of degrading encounters as Bill became less concerned with her and positively obsessed with getting her pregnant. It was obvious to her they were trying too hard, but her arguments fell on deaf ears.

They fought constantly, and Rachel began to question her reasons for marrying Bill in the first place. Where were the gentleness, the concern, the mutual cooperation so desperately needed if they wanted to start a family? Rachel suggested consulting a doctor, and Bill exploded in rage, as if she had doubted his manhood.

From that point on their marriage became a nightmare. The only blessing was that Bill, increasingly sullen and antagonistic, never touched her again. He later informed her he had been to a doctor who told him he was all right. He acted as if she were tainted now, and he never let her forget that she was less than whole or that she had let him down by not having his child. At last, after three years of marriage, he filed for divorce, and Rachel was only too happy to go along.

The memories caused her no pain now, even though it had been an especially bitter separation. She had long since reshaped her life and was happy just as she was. Though there had been friendly liaisons, teasing and flirtatious relationships since then, she had truly never felt the need for a man's constant companionship. But now the intensity with which her feelings flowed toward Zachary frightened her. It was as if a barrier had been breached, but it was a barrier Rachel could not remember building. She felt Zachary's hand brush her arm.

"Hey, I'm sorry if I brought back unwanted memories. I didn't mean to break the spell I'm trying to cast on you," he said softly.

Rachel smiled. There was a gentleness to Zachary despite his imposing masculinity. He was indeed casting a spell over her—a spell she didn't want to avoid. "I'd rather not talk about it if you don't mind."

"Why should I mind?" he replied with a warm smile. "The last thing I want to discuss with you is another man." He took her empty glass from her hand and set it down beside his own. "To be really truthful, I don't feel much like talking at all right now," he said in a husky voice. His hand, surprisingly gentle for its size, reached out to trace the delicate angles of her cheek and chin, sending a shiver rippling through her. His fingers wandered downward, softly stroking the sensitive skin of her neck, then entwined in her hair, pulling her gently toward his demanding lips. "Sweet Rachel," he murmured as he hungrily took possession of her mouth, sipping at her lips as if she were a fine wine.

Rachel's pulse pounded in her ears, her breath quickening as his lips strayed from her mouth to her throat. He pulled her against his chest as her hands slipped around his sides underneath his coat, caressing the tense muscles of his back. Still, it wasn't enough. She wanted to feel his skin beneath her hands, feel the crisp hair of his chest against her aching breasts. "Zachary—"

"I know," he said, crushing her against him. "I feel it, too."

He picked her up as if she weighed nothing, cradled her body against his, and carried her to a huge master bedroom. All thoughts of why she had originally wanted to go to dinner with him this evening were long gone, washed away by her tremendous need and his reverent touch.

After removing his tie, Rachel feverishly unbuttoned his shirt, letting her hands have free rein over his body. The tips of her fingers discovered the muscles, angles, and lines of his masculine chest, and she pressed him intimately against her body.

Zachary burned to possess her, and soon her dress and a lacy sheer bra lay in a pool of light at Rachel's feet. He pressed her feverishly against him, slipping his hands intimately into the waist of her pantyhose, his hands gliding lower, cupping her bottom and moving against Rachel to make her even more aware of his burning passion. He moved his body back a little to allow her to further her own explorations. She quickly removed his pants; her hands slid downward, her fingers entering the next barrier without hesitation.

"Rachel, sweet Rachel, what you're doing to me." He groaned, his hands moving even more daringly now. He wanted to taste her, all of her, smell her alluring scent upon his body, feel her flesh surrounding his.

She held her breath, her skin tingling with anticipation and desire. A soft gasp escaped her as his gentle fingers slid sweetly, knowingly against her and then slowly away. As he gradually removed her pantyhose, he tasted and touched every inch of her honeyed thighs. Kissing and tracing the shape of her calves, smoothing over her ankles to her toes, Zachary drew out the anticipation with maddening expertise.

"Zachary, please—" she moaned as he worked his way tenderly up her body, stroking her soft belly, skirting around her breasts to her waiting lips. Zachary plunged deeply into her willing mouth, their tongues joining in fire.

Rachel's breasts ached once again for his fiery touch, her senses bursting with the need for more and the sure knowledge of what was to come. Raining kisses down his throat, she nibbled his tanned skin, then caressed his nipples to hardness.

Cupping her breasts, he slowly caressed each treasure, marveling at their beautiful shape. His passion increased at her quick responsiveness to his every motion. His tongue flicked their rosy peaks into hardness, and then his mouth gently softened them again.

Rachel was lost in pleasure, wanting this to go on forever yet yearning for release from the delicious torment. Her mind and body whirled as wave after wave of sensation moved her more closely to their joining. The tension building in her was as tight as a newly coiled spring ready to burst forth.

"Zachary, yes, oh, yes," she cried, arching up to meet him as he joined her waiting flesh with his.

Coherent thought left them when they came together in ecstatic joy, a savage, almost desperate passion taking its place.

Afterward Rachel stretched full-length on her stomach, Zachary's strong hands caressing the damp skin of her back. "There is an unbelievable fire beneath that icy exterior," he told her softly. "I'm surprised we didn't both go up in flames."

"It's been a long time," she murmured, feeling a delicious exhaustion.

"Anyone since your husband?" he asked.

"None of your business," she replied with mock severity.

His laughter tickled her cheek as she cuddled against him and soon fell fast asleep.

Zachary was sleeping peacefully when she awoke the next morning. That didn't surprise her much after their repeated and exquisite lovemaking of last night. She had always been an early riser, rarely able to sleep past sunrise. He was lying on his stomach, the sheet thrown low across his hips, revealing the strong lines of his shoulders tapering into lean hips and firm buttocks. Even in sleep she could see the strength in his body. She wanted to stroke the tanned skin till she woke him, then make him aware of her every need. But he was sleeping peacefully, his breathing even and relaxed. She could wait awhile, savor her thoughts. Deciding not to wake him, she got up and stretched languorously, took a quick shower and dressed. She went downstairs, thinking to surprise him with breakfast, but before that she decided to take another look at his cars.

Rachel had always loved the early mornings here in the country, with the humid air and dew-covered grass. Tree frogs scampered out of her path as she made her way to the garage. The smell of lush growth surrounded her, overwhelming her senses, a feeling of peace settling around her. She arrived at the garage and, after turning on the lights, gave a loving pat to the two cars within.

The building was divided into sections, as the old stables must have been, with a car in each section and then Zachary's toolroom. She realized that there must be one more section, judging from the length of the place, and sure enough she found another door on the far side of the toolroom wall. *This must be where he keeps his American car,* she thought as she stepped through the door into another stall. She was only half right. What she saw nearly caused her heart to stop, a sudden rush of shock and severe disillusionment assaulting her mind.

There, in all its magnificent bulk, showing the

same signs of prideful ownership Zachary's other cars did, was the Duesenberg. Not another one, as she first thought before checking it over carefully, but the same one—the one she thought was crushed and sitting in her service shop.

She was glad the car hadn't been destroyed. It was a fine example of the American auto builders' art. But why had Zachary pretended to have it crushed? More to the point, why had he continued his deception when he had the opportunity to show her the car last night?

Was it because he was afraid he wouldn't be able to get her into bed after showing her he'd deceived her? If so, he was most certainly correct in his assumption! Who did he think he was, some tin god to go around manipulating people to suit him?

Granted, the events of last evening had led to a wonderful conclusion, and it had been far from a one-sided seduction. Even now the memory of Zachary's sensual touch and body made her shiver with delight. While it was true she had started out the evening intending to pave the way for a real estate transaction, much more had taken place.

No, Rachel wasn't sorry last night had happened. She'd wanted Zachary as much as he appeared to want her. But what was he up to, and what was she going to do about it?

She knew she was much too angry and upset to think clearly, so she decided not to let her thoughts linger on what had happened between them. There would be time enough for that later.

First off, she had to even up the score for Zachary's little joke. She would listen when the time came, for after all, she still needed his parcel of land. But he had to pay for the torment he'd put her and her staff through. As she walked inside with every intention of waking him up in some dastardly way or another, a much more appropriate idea came to her.

First, she called herself a cab. Then she dialed the number of a local landscaping firm. "This is Rachel Jordan. You did some work for me at Jordan Motorcars a while back."

"Yes, Miss Jordan, I remember you well. What can we do for you today?"

"A friend of mine needs to get his garden in order," she said, smiling wickedly. "I'd like you to make a delivery this morning to his house and charge it to me."

CHAPTER THREE

Zachary was awakened by a loud noise, but by the time he was fully awake the noise had stopped. Rachel was nowhere to be found. Assuming she had gone out for a walk, he pulled on a pair of faded jeans and went to the front door, where he found a note taped at eye level. He read it aloud. "Dear Zachary: This is what you're full of."

Confused, he opened the door and was immediately hit by an incredibly foul odor. He stepped out onto his porch to see what was causing the stench, his eyes widening in disbelief. In the middle of his driveway, blocking it completely, was a very large pile of steer manure, its overwhelming fragrance hanging in the muggy morning air.

* * *

No service or office work was performed on Saturdays at Jordan Motorcars, but the sales crew was much in evidence when Rachel arrived. They were quite mystified by her bright eyes and happy step until she explained about the Duesenberg and the early-morning delivery to Zachary's house. Of course, she omitted how she had come to be at his home in the first place, and they tactfully didn't inquire.

Rachel had a long-standing policy of allowing her employees to take care of their own cars on the weekends, and she enlisted their aid in moving the crushed car into the showroom, with the idea of using it in some sort of sales promotion or another. Perhaps she could find out what kind of car it had really been, then have a contest, with some free service work for the person who guessed the correct make and model.

Usually she spent the day going over the books, and she tried to do so; but her eyes kept straying to the phone, waiting for the call she knew had to come. Zachary didn't bother phoning, though. He didn't even bother to knock. He simply burst into her office, looking as though he'd like to throttle her.

"My, that was fast!" she exclaimed, giving him a wide grin.

"Lyons Construction, remember? I called in a front-end loader and moved it in five minutes." His voice now held an edge that cut like an arctic wind.

Her grin disappeared. "The idea was to let

you think about your crimes for a while," she replied, well able to make her own voice sound cold as ice.

He sat casually on the edge of her desk, his expression guarded. "And what crime might that be, sweet Rachel?" he asked, reaching his hand out and running a gentle finger across her cheek. "Making love to you?"

Damn him and his rapid mood changes! His touch caused a ripple of excitement, and she cursed her body for its betrayal. "You know very well that's not what I'm talking about."

"Then why did you leave?"

"I decided there wasn't any reason to stay. You got what you wanted."

The corner of his mouth pulled up with the hint of a smile. "Not nearly enough. How about you?"

"I see I was right. You really are full of it!" she retorted, her eyes widening at his outrageous comment.

He smiled fully now. "Temper, temper. There's no reason to get mad at me because you won't admit to your own desires."

Rachel blocked out the picture forming in her mind. Zachary lying in bed, a sheet thrown low over his hips . . . "I—I," she sputtered, then took a deep breath to calm herself. "All I desire right now," she said through clenched teeth, "is to know what that damn Duesenberg is doing in your garage."

He ran a hand thoughtfully over his clean-shaven face. "I take it you did some exploring this morning," he said.

Rachel nodded. "Made an interesting discovery, too," she replied sharply.

"I can explain."

"I'm listening." *This should be good,* she thought. She was tempted to smile but wasn't quite through watching his discomfort. It was time to turn the tables on him.

"As you know, I like to do most of my own work, but there are things I can't do well enough to suit me, so I brought the Duesenberg in. I wanted to watch and said so." He shrugged his shoulders. "You would have thought I had impugned your mechanic's honor or something."

"Mechanics are like that. It's rather like telling a surgeon you want to watch him operate on you."

Zachary stood up, a smile on his face, and sat down in the chair in front of her. "Yes, well, all I wanted was to learn a few things. It's to your staff's favor that they eventually allowed me to stay. As you also know, I'm a perfectionist and a bit impetuous."

"A bit," Rachel interjected sardonically.

"I'm afraid I couldn't help offering a few suggestions."

"Cardinal sin," she said dramatically, thoroughly enjoying herself now.

"Evidently. To make a long story short, I got mad, they got mad, and my car and I left. After

I had cooled down, I tried to make another appointment, but no one wanted to work on my car anymore."

"I can't imagine why." Rachel chuckled. She could no longer hold back a grin. "To be fair, we really are understaffed. They would have gotten around to you eventually. You didn't help matters any, though. Did you really tell Martin you wouldn't even let him work on your heavy construction equipment if he paid you?"

Zachary cleared his throat. "Or words to that effect."

"So you decided to pay us back, is that it?" she asked.

"Seemed like a good idea at the time."

"That impetuous nature of yours almost got you clobbered," she pointed out. "Being a classic car lover yourself, you should have realized my staff wanted to kill you when they thought you'd crushed that car."

"I've been in a few brawls," he replied with a cocky air. "I was an oil field worker, remember? Anyway," he continued, his expression softening, "I didn't know I was going to meet such a fascinating woman at the wheel of this organization."

Rachel didn't return his smile. She still wasn't satisfied. "If I'm so fascinating, why didn't you show me the Duesenberg last night?"

"I had other matters on my mind," he said, his black eyes gleaming.

"That's no excuse for deceiving me, and

47

deception isn't a nice way to begin a relationship."

"I couldn't agree more. My only defense is that I wanted to be on more . . . friendly terms with you before I told you. I assume that was your intention as well?" His eyebrows arched to emphasize his question.

Rachel frowned. "What's that supposed to mean?"

"It means that I wasn't the only one waiting for the right time to say something."

"I wasn't implying that you seduced me against my will, but—"

"Come now, Rachel," he broke in, "you know perfectly well what I'm talking about. I may be a busy man, and I freely admit I wanted you in my bed the moment I saw you." He paused, enjoying the startled look on her face. "But I know each and every one of my property holdings, and you told me yourself about your need to expand. Did you think I wasn't listening to you?" he asked intently.

"Well, I—"

"Just who was deceiving whom?"

She had to fight to keep her expression from registering her shock. "You know I'm interested in your land?" she managed to ask.

"Of course, though I hope that's not the only reason you spent the night with me."

Rachel hadn't blushed since her schoolgirl days, but she fought hard to keep her face from coloring now. That had nothing to do with the land. "What a horrible thing to say!"

Zachary shrugged. "Only if it's true," he returned calmly. "It's not, is it?" He watched her face closely.

"Of course not!" she cried, standing and crossing her arms over her breasts in a defensive gesture. "What kind of woman do you suppose I am?"

Zachary stood up, too. He came around the desk and grasped her gently by the shoulders. "You are the most intelligent, fascinating, and passionate woman I've ever met."

"You've seen all the passion you're going to see," she said, trying to break free of his grasp. Whom was she kidding? Being this close to him already had her heart pounding.

Heedless of her struggles, Zachary wrapped his arms around her. "We've only just whetted our appetites for each other, Rachel. There's much more to come," he said seductively before taking possession of her mouth.

Suddenly it ceased to matter that he had deceived her or that he had known about her own deception. Her anger dissipated more with each ragged breath, and her hands wandered of their own volition to the back of his neck, her fingers tangling in his coal black hair. When he finally released her, she felt as if the temperature of the room had climbed by several degrees.

Rachel could no longer deny the need that burned so intensely within her. However, she was afraid to let this impetuous and unpredictable man carry her headlong into uncharted and dangerous waters. Stepping farther away from him, she drew a breath, fighting to bring her emotions under control. "Will you sell me your land?" she asked.

Zachary threw back his head in open laughter. "That depends," he said, a devilish gleam in his eyes.

"On what?" she asked warily.

"On the terms," his sensual voice replied.

"Zachary . . ." she began heatedly.

"On how our negotiations proceed," he continued with a wicked smile.

"Let's keep business business, Zachary," she warned.

"Exactly. What kind of, um, business did you have in mind, Rachel?"

"The land, Zachary, as in the property next door," she said, exasperated.

"Oh. That business," he said regretfully.

"Well?"

"Well what?"

"Quit playing with me, Zachary. Do you want to sell me the land or not?"

He looked as if he were contemplating the question deeply, but a spark of laughter remained in his eyes. "I don't think I'll ever want to quit playing with you, Rachel. But, yes, I'll sell you the land. I'd even be willing to carry the loan, provided I can be sure of your ability to repay."

Her eyes narrowed. "What the hell do you mean?"

"Steady, dear. I mean, to satisfy my accountant, I'll need to know your business better. Since you, essentially, are the business, I guess we'll just have to spend some time together. Personally, that's what I had in mind all along," he said, caressing her cheek with the back of his hand.

"Oh." Her temper cooled. "I think that can be arranged," she said slyly. "You can start by taking me to lunch. With all my activity this morning, I forgot breakfast."

"Yes, you were a busy little devil this morning, weren't you?"

"What did you do with all that fertilizer anyway?" she asked curiously.

"I returned it," he replied as he took her arm and opened the office door for her.

"To the landscaper?"

He smiled and shook his head. "To the sender. I had my crew dump it on your apartment patio."

"You didn't!" she cried in horror.

"No, but I should have." Zachary laughed. "Now, what would you like for lunch?"

Rachel sighed with relief. "Anything. I'm famished."

"Well, I'll take you anywhere except a steak house. I've suddenly developed an aversion to cows."

* * *

In the next few weeks Rachel and Zachary spent a good deal of time together, all of it, especially the nights, happily.

Eventually Zachary—and his accountant—seemed satisfied with Rachel's financial responsibility, and contracts were drawn up and signed for the land. It actually worked out better than Rachel thought it would because Zachary agreed to have his company design and build the addition. This gave her an opportunity to get to know him on a business level too. She liked what she saw.

If Zachary was impulsive with his personal life, Rachel found he was exactly the opposite in his business dealings. He managed his company thoughtfully and confidently. Rachel had to admit that as a businessman he was tough but fair. The price he asked for his land and his services was market value—no more no less.

The sound of Zachary's MG alerted his foreman to his arrival at the job site just before quitting time, and the burly man met him at the security fence. They had a short discussion. Then Zachary turned his attention to the real reason he had come—Rachel.

In the weeks since the incident with the crushed car Zachary had managed to convince Rachel's staff that their image of him as an unfeeling monster was completely unfounded. Even Martin, the chief mechanic Rachel had threatened Zachary with, had warmed up considerably. Zachary met the intelligent, wiry man as he strolled through the service shop on his way to see Rachel.

"Hey, Martin, looks like you're working hard."

Martin, leaning comfortably against the counter of the toolroom, looked up and smiled amiably at the friendly gibe. "Doesn't look as if you've been climbing around many of your job sites today, Zach," he said, looking disdainfully at the other's tan business suit.

Zachary sighed heavily. "Yeah, that's the way it is with us entrepreneurial types. The only thing we get dirty is our fingertips from counting money." He knew full well Martin was doing exactly what he wanted to do and that his criticism was just Martin's way of being friendly.

Martin chuckled. "I would have thought you hired someone to count your money for you."

"Oh, no," Zachary returned with a grin, "I have this cute young thing that helps me, though. Much more fun that way."

"What!" Rachel cried as she came into the room and overheard the conversation.

"Just kidding," Zachary said, his grin widening. He looked her over as if they had just met. He still couldn't get over how lovely she was.

"Sure," she returned, her heart skipping a beat at the warmth of his gaze.

Martin pushed himself away from the counter and held up his hand in a pacifying gesture. "Not that I wouldn't just love to see you two have a knock-down, drag-out, but it's time to go home. I've got enough overtime this week." He started away from them but then turned. "How's the Duesenberg?" he asked Zachary.

"Perfect."

Martin waved away the comment. "I know that. I did the work when you finally brought her back in. I was only wondering if you'd managed to destroy it in a week."

"As a matter of fact," Zachary returned with an air of mock insult, "I plan to use it tonight to take Rachel out on the town." He looked at her. "If she's free."

"No accounting for taste," Martin quipped. "Just remember not to push her over sixty; she's still breaking in new piston rings."

"The Duesie or Rachel?" Zachary asked.

"Hey!" Rachel interjected.

"Night, all," Martin shot back over his shoulder as he walked away, shaking his head and laughing.

Rachel faced Zachary, her hands on her hips, a sparkle in her eyes. "I don't see you in three days, and here I find you demeaning me in front of the help."

"I couldn't demean you if I tried," he said, stepping closer to her. He savored the smell of her perfume, the nearness of her. "Besides, Martin is even fonder of you than he is of that ancient Rolls-Royce he drives."

"I doubt that. He rebuilt it from the ground up." She looked into his black eyes, sparkling with the enjoyment of seeing her again. Her pulse raced crazily. She had missed him, missed his satirical sense of humor.

"I missed you," he said as if reading her thoughts.

"It was only three days," she responded, thinking it had seemed more like three weeks. "How much could you miss me in three days?"

He stepped even closer to her until she could feel the warmth of his body and smell his after-shave even through the motor oil smell of the shop. "Have dinner with me tonight, and I'll show you," he answered, his deep voice full of sensual promise.

"And if I don't?" she said playfully.

Zachary took her in his arms so swiftly she gasped, her voice sounding loud in the now-empty service shop. "Then I'll carry you off to your office and show you right there," he growled before his mouth lowered to hers.

Their tongues touched, swirling with the deep need and emotion they both felt. But the place was too public for their passion, and the kiss ended, reluctantly, only whetting their appetites.

"I'll need to go home and get ready." It was as much as she could say while trying to gain control of her breathing.

"See you at seven," he replied. He looked at her as if drinking in the sight of her, kissed her again softly, then turned and left.

Rachel collected her thoughts and went about the business of closing down for the night. Then she went to her apartment to shower and change. While she did so, her thoughts wandered over the rapid changes in her life.

Rachel was, and essentially always had been, a happy person, taking the ups and downs of life with equal grace. When things went well, she enjoyed them; when they went badly, she worked harder. To get where she was, she had worked like a maniac for the past five years, more if she included her self-imposed apprenticeship in the business, and now she was enjoying the fruits of her labor. She worked on the design of the addition to Jordan Motorcars and, when construction began, lovingly observed its progress. Zachary and she went to candlelit restaurants, plays, operas, and even worked out together in the complete gym he had at his home. In fact, Zachary was slowly becoming very much a part of her life. And that was the only frightening thing in an otherwise satisfying relationship.

It was what lay in the past, she knew, that gave her relationship with Zachary such disturbing overtones. After her divorce she found herself single and in pain, with no job and an extremely low opinion of herself. Her father had passed on several years earlier; her mother had become ensconced in the upper-class society Bill's family circulated in, and she felt unwilling to put her at odds with it. The only thing she had was a pretty British sports car Bill had given her as a wedding present. It was the only thing she kept or would accept from him. She sold it, made enough to get another car and move to Houston, where she stayed with friends and began to pull the threads of her life back together again.

All that lay behind her, far enough behind not to hurt anymore. It had, however, changed her life and the way she looked at things. She knew she had been very fortunate in the last few years. She was a successful businesswoman, secure and happy with her achievements. The trials of the past had tempered her personality, made her strong, self-sufficient, and confident in her own abilities. Her life had taken a different focus from most, and she was glad it had.

Zachary did not seem to be threatened by her intelligence and thirst for success. Bill had been. Zachary was kind and gentle, and when they were together, she felt certain he genuinely cared for her. Indeed, Zachary had become a strong presence in her life, causing her to wonder about the self-sufficiency she cultivated.

The doorbell rang, and Rachel ran to answer it, quieting the rising feeling of anticipation she felt at Zachary's arrival. The feeling came flooding back when she opened the door. She doubted she would ever get tired of looking at him—or of the way he looked at her.

"Hello, Rachel," he said softly, his gaze roving over her as if for the first time. "Perhaps I'll cancel our reservations. You look edible enough to me."

She turned around once, giving him the full effect of the soft gray silk dress she wore. When she looked into his eyes again, she could see the desire he felt for her. "Like it?"

In way of answer he pulled her close and kissed her. "How hungry are you?" he murmured.

"Ravenous." Her eyes sparkled with humor.

Zachary sighed. "One appetite at a time, I suppose?"

"Definitely."

They went arm in arm to the parking garage, Rachel laughing when she saw the Duesenberg. He had parked it sideways across three spaces. "The management frowns on this sort of thing," she told him.

"I tried putting it in one space. The sides hung over the lines by a few feet and the tail stuck out into the driveway, so I figured this was the logical thing to do."

They purred toward their destination, drawing interested and sometimes amazed stares from the other drivers on the freeways. In a city where a Rolls-Royce warranted barely a glance and exotic sports cars filled the parking lots, the Duesenberg was still capable of attracting attention.

Rachel smiled at Zachary as he lovingly piloted the big car. "Makes you feel just a little decadent."

He grinned and nodded in agreement. "Nothing like conspicuous consumption, I always say."

The parking valet tried to look as if he had seen such cars all evening but finally broke down and told Zachary he would keep a special eye on it while they were inside. They were shown to a table where Zachary ordered for them both. Then they settled down to enjoy the restaurant's elegant atmosphere while they waited for their dinner to arrive.

"Did you have a good time in Dallas?" Rachel asked. He had gone there to inspect some property he was interested in.

"I couldn't wait to get back."

"How did the property look?"

"I couldn't concentrate on it. All I could see was the way you looked before I left, with the covers pulled up to your nose and that wicked gleam in your eyes," he replied in a low voice.

"Zachary"—Rachel admonished him with a laugh—"I'm trying to make small talk."

He reached across the table and took her hand, his skin smooth and warm against hers. "Let's skip to dessert and go home."

It was tempting, as was the warmth of his touch, but the waiter arrived to serve them at that moment, so they stayed and enjoyed the marvelous food. They both unconsciously hurried through their dinner.

"I've been meaning to ask you, but we've both been so busy," Rachel said while they finished the wine. "What kind of car was that you had crushed? I'm going to have a contest to guess it at our grand opening of the addition."

Zachary chuckled. "Then everybody will have two chances to win. It's a Ford with a Volkswagen thrown in for good measure. One car didn't make a big enough block."

"You"—Rachel sniffed—"are incorrigible."

"Guilty," he replied. "And you," he continued, his eyes flashing sensually, "have one chance to finish your drink before I pick you up and carry you out of here."

The tip of her tongue ran temptingly across her bottom lip. "You wouldn't dare," she said tauntingly, looking at him through lowered lashes.

Zachary's eyebrows raised in challenge. "Hah!"

"People would stare."

He started to rise. "I like conspicuous consumption, remember?"

Rachel considered taunting him further, but she knew he was outrageous enough to carry out his threat. They left the restaurant in a civilized, if giddy, manner, with no doubt where they were going.

It was strange, she thought, how well Zachary and she got along. They both had strong personalities and were devoted to their careers. Their lives had been full and happy before they met, but now the time they spent together seemed more precious than anything else. She was becoming very attached to him and could tell he felt the same. That worried her a bit, but she didn't dwell on it. She decided the best thing to do was to let their relationship take its natural course.

They barely made it through her door before they fell into an embrace, close and warm and ripe with promise. It seemed only a few breathless, exciting moments before they lay side by side on Rachel's big four-poster canopied bed, rediscovering each other with delight.

Zachary's strong yet gentle hands cupped each of her breasts in turn, his palms starting and his tongue finishing the task of bringing her nipples to an exquisitely pleasurable hardness. With maddeningly slow strokes he caressed her back, across her waist and down over her buttocks, his soft touch lingering on her center before brushing against her hips and stomach, then back to her breasts to begin again.

Her hands wandered intimately over the muscles of his back, chest, and slim hips, boldly taking possession of him. His thighs were strong and powerful; his muscled frame was well defined yet graceful. She shivered with the sheer pleasure of touching him.

"Where have you been all my life, sweet Rachel?" he asked huskily.

She gasped when his caress returned once again to the sensitive skin of her inner thighs, followed quickly by his tongue and gentle nips of his teeth. "I've—I've been waiting for you to teach me all these delicious things." She gasped again, the sparkle of mischief in her smoldering gaze.

"Ah! Well, I'll just have to show you how well I've learned my lessons, won't I?" he murmured against her skin.

When at last neither could take the torment any longer, Zachary wrapped his arm around her waist and pulled her to him, joining them as one. The gentle rhythm he initiated became their whole world until they collapsed in each other's arms, only to begin again when their breath returned to normal. It was a sensual, dizzying merry-go-round, and Rachel never wanted to get off.

In the morning they had breakfast. Rachel put sweet rolls in the oven to bake while she showered and almost burned them when Zachary surprised her in the shower. Afterward they prepared to go to work but lingered in each other's arms till they both were late.

"How about tonight?" Zachary asked.

"What did you have in mind?" she replied innocently, her eyes full of wicked lights.

"Tennis, maybe a swim, then dinner at my place."

She smiled. "Sounds good. Oh, by the way, I have to go to an auction on Saturday," Rachel told him as he put on his suit coat. She straightened his tie. "Would you like to come?"

"Will you go without me if I don't?"

"I have to."

"Then I'll come."

She chuckled and walked him to the door,

giving him a slight shove on his way out. "Nice to know I have such persuasive powers."

He leaned back and kissed her, then took off at a near run. Rachel looked at her watch, dashed to grab her purse and briefcase, and passed him in the hall.

CHAPTER FOUR

Friday, after a delicious session of physical exercise at Zachary's house—not all of which took place in his well-equipped gym—Rachel spent the night and in the morning prepared for the car auction east of Houston. They packed a picnic lunch and left early, planning to spend some time looking over the cars before the sale. To Rachel the trip wasn't entirely a day off. She was interested in a few of the cars being sold.

A beautiful morning turned into a gorgeous day. It wasn't too hot, and the sun shone brightly. When they arrived at the park where the auction was to take place, they found themselves part of the show. Zachary had decided to take his elegant white Jaguar and, along with the other participants in the auction who came in classic cars, was directed to park in a reserved area that quickly became the center of attention. Indeed, some of those present seemed more interested in the potential bidders' cars than they were in the machines for sale.

Rachel went ahead to find seats in a special section reserved for serious collectors and dealers. She met up with an amused Zachary a few minutes later. "What's so funny?" she asked.

"Some guy just made a ridiculous offer on my Jag."

"Auction loonies," she said knowingly. She pointed to a rather unusual group of people who were looking over the cars for sale and talking animatedly among themselves. "There's the real competition."

Zachary observed them for a moment. "They look as if they can barely tolerate each other," he said.

"Astute observation. Those are competitors of mine, and they form what is known in auction circles as a ring. You'll find them at almost every sale within a five-hundred-mile radius."

He nodded. "I thought they looked familiar."

"You've been to these affairs before?" she asked in surprise.

"On occasion," he replied simply. "The ring decides which cars they want, then carefully avoids bidding against each other, right?"

She looked at him skeptically, deciding he knew more than he was about to tell. "Right. Then later they auction off their purchases among themselves and split the difference in price between the first and second auction."

"Sounds like a good way to keep prices down. Why aren't you in with them?"

"For one thing, they aren't very good at it. For another, I usually buy in the unrestored category, and few of them have the facilities or the inclination for restoration," she explained.

"Besides, you don't like them, do you?" he asked.

"Does it show?"

"To me it does." Zachary kissed her lightly on the nose. "Anyway, it doesn't really matter, I suppose. There are no friends at an auction. Shall we go register as bidders?"

"We?"

He smiled innocently. "You don't expect me to miss out on all the fun, do you?"

They both found things to interest them among the diverse machinery up for sale. Rachel picked two cars she wanted at the right price and another she might be willing to go out on a limb for. This particular automobile, a gracefully aging Bentley, would sell almost before she could do some necessary restoration and get it on her showroom floor. With her company's capabilities, it would be nearly impossible for the ring to beat her bid and still make a profit.

Zachary, however, had come across an entirely different kind of interesting tidbit. Though definitely not in the same category as Rachel's choices, the slightly battered Triumph still put a definite gleam in his eyes.

"You do seem to be overly fond of English cars," Rachel noted, looking at the distressed sports car with a mixture of disdain and pity. "But this one's had a rather hard life."

"Don't you insult her!" Zachary replied. He patted a rumpled fender. "She just needs some loving attention, don't you, old girl?"

Rachel stifled a giggle. She could see him now, in his faded overalls, lavishing much-needed care on the abused vehicle. She realized his sometimes eccentric behavior was part of his charm.

Attending auctions had become an increasingly important part of Rachel's business. There were other ways of obtaining the cars she needed, of course, such as selling on consignment or purchasing directly from collectors. These methods reduced her profit, however, for it was a rare occurrence indeed these days to find a private owner who didn't know the value of his or her car. Apart from the necessity of attending auctions, Rachel simply enjoyed the proceedings immensely.

The excitement among the crowd increased with every car that was rolled in front of the auctioneer. The ring was much in evidence, buying heavily, and Rachel watched with dismay as the first of her choices quickly rose beyond her self-imposed bid limit.

The ring wasn't interested in the Bentley,

however, and bidding was sluggish. When the auctioneer announced that there was a reserve, or bottom limit, on the car, the other dealers seemed even less inclined to pursue it.

Thanks to some rather unusual and mysteriously sophisticated bidding signals from Zachary, Rachel and he worked as a team to purchase both the Bentley and his beloved Triumph for well under market value.

"Just where did you learn to bid covert signals like that?" Rachel asked, the glow of success reddening her cheeks.

"Wait till you see the signals I want to work on later," he growled before taking possession of her lips.

They settled their debts, thanked the auctioneer, who told them that theirs was the strangest bidding style he had ever seen, and arranged to have the cars delivered to Rachel's shop. Then they went to a deserted glen not far from town for their picnic. The grass was soft and green, the sky a brilliant blue, and a light breeze gently rustled the leaves of the giant shade tree above their heads as they ate.

After they had hungrily consumed fried chicken, potato salad, and chocolate cake, Zachary leaned lightly against the tree with Rachel's head in his lap while they shared the remainder of the wine he had brought.

"That was fantastic, Rachel." Zachary sighed contentedly. "Did you really cook all that?"

She reached up and swatted him lightly on the forehead. "Mosquito," she explained.

"Sorry. You just seem to be constantly full of surprises."

"I'm not all beauty and brains, Zachary." She admonished him with a laugh. "And you have a few mysteries up your sleeve, too."

He looked into her eyes and shrugged. "You mean the auction? My father was a part-time auctioneer for twenty years before he passed on. Drove my mother crazy. She collected carnival glass, and he was constantly selling her collections."

"See what I mean? You never told me that before."

"You never asked."

Rachel swatted the imaginary mosquito again. He grabbed her hand and kissed her palm, his tongue tracing a pattern on the sensitive skin. "We did work well together, didn't we?" he asked.

She nodded her reply as he unbuttoned her shirt, his hand gently caressing her breasts as he released them from their lacy covering. She gasped with pleasure when he bent to close his lips on first one hard-tipped peak, then the other.

Rachel lay back, smiling up at Zachary, enjoying him, the sunshine, and their time together. Her hands found the bottom of his navy blue polo shirt and started inching the material upward to the top of his chest, where she met resistance. "Zachary, cooperate," Rachel murmured.

"I'm busy at the moment," he replied, his hands greedily enjoying the pleasures of her body, his eyes sparkling at the sight of her silky, smooth skin glistening in the sun.

"You won't be for long," Rachel said threateningly, "if you don't help me. I want your shirt off. Right now," she whispered sensually.

Zachary didn't move or change positions. Laughing, he looked down at her, then finally bent to whisper into her ear. "And just what will you do if I don't do as ordered, sweet Rachel? Ravish me?" he said hopefully. His tongue delicately traced the soft shell-like contours of her ear before nipping playfully at the lobe. "Hmm. No snappy comeback. You're slipping, Rachel," he said tauntingly, waiting for her reaction.

It was swift in coming. Zachary found himself on his back, Rachel laughing at the look on his face as she scrambled on top of him. He hugged her close, breathing in her own special scent, and kissed her, a deep kiss filled with silent promises. His gentle hand brushed an errant lock of dark brown hair from her face. "I've been thinking quite a bit about us lately," he said softly. "We work well together, play well together, have many interests in common. Our appetites even match perfectly." His voice turned husky, and he buried his face in the soft skin of her neck, his teeth nipping her delicately before rising once more to her mouth. "I love the way our bodies fit together, too."

Rachel looked into his eyes, a worried frown creasing her forehead at the seriousness she found there. "Zachary—"

"I have something I want to ask you, Rachel," he said, interrupting her. His voice was as serious as his expression. Then he noticed her worried look. "What's wrong?"

She got to her feet and smiled, though her thoughts were far from light. "Will you excuse me?"

"What? Oh, certainly. Second tree on the left."

"Men!" She chuckled. "You have it so easy. Just find a convenient tree."

"Hurry back," he replied, watching as she rearranged her clothes and wandered over the hill.

Rachel wasn't heeding the call of nature, though. She needed to be alone for a while. She found a secluded spot and sat down on a fallen tree, feeling confused and disturbed.

Zachary wasn't the only one who had been thinking about their relationship. What he said was true. They did fit together well, mind and body. The past month was the happiest in her memory, so why should she feel the way she did? The answer, of course, was Zachary. His attitude toward her when they were alone had recently grown more serious. She knew the question he was about to ask, just as she knew the answer she would have to give if she couldn't somehow prevent him from asking. She needed time to be sure of just what was happening to her.

Their relationship until now had been caring and giving, building within her a contentment she had never known. Zachary seemed to be everything she had been searching for. He was fun-loving and carefree, involved in his own business, and quite obviously a confirmed bachelor. So why was he going to spoil everything by getting so serious?

Rachel had had enough seriousness in her life. Though she believed without a doubt her previous marriage had been a bad one and would have broken up anyway, the problem that had spelled the end had been her inability to provide Bill with children. It was an inability she hadn't taken personally until the night Bill came home, drunk from what he said was a celebration, and announced he had seen a doctor. "I'm all man," he had said caustically. "You're the one with the problem. It seems I didn't marry a complete woman. Hell, you're not a woman at all!"

The words had hurt, but not half as much as the resulting disruption the divorce caused in her life. She was busy getting back on her feet again, so it was a long time before thoughts of her supposed infertility had led her to a doctor. Though vague, he assured her she was sterile. Meanwhile, Bill had been running his own tests, and they turned out to be conclusive—and irrefutable. Three years after the divorce, at Christmas, she received a card with a picture enclosed. The photograph showed Bill, his new wife, Claire, and a baby boy. Claire was also pregnant again.

Rachel sighed and got up from the log she was sitting on. Why did things have to be so complicated? She enjoyed Zachary's company, she loved to be with him, but she saw no reason to get married. Marriage was for people who wanted to start families. Since she couldn't have children and was happy with her business and her private life, why complicate matters?

Cresting the hill and picking her way carefully down to their picnic spot, she saw Zachary waiting where she had left him. He was a virile, handsome man who may have decided it was time to settle down, she thought. No matter what he told her concerning children, eventually a man like him would want a child of his own, a child she couldn't give him. It had turned Bill into a monster, and Rachel would never go through that anguish again—never. Nor would she put Zachary into that kind of situation.

Zachary was having another piece of chocolate cake. "I was about to send out a search party," he commented.

Rachel forced herself to smile. What was she going to do? She still wanted to see him, didn't want to think about doing without him, but that was the problem: Zachary had become an important part of her life that she didn't want to do without.

How, Rachel thought as she looked at his smiling face, *do you tactfully tell a man you want to continue seeing him yet want to cool your sexual relationship for a while till you're thinking straight? You don't.* But if things continued the way they were, she wouldn't be able to say no to Zachary's proposal. His powerful masculinity wove too great a spell over her. She needed to stop and think. Zachary, or any man she might marry, had a right to know about her inability to have children—before they were married. Rachel knew she would have to tell Zachary about her problems and then hope that he still cared for her.

"Ready for that question I want to ask you?" he said as if in confirmation of her thoughts.

He wanted more, but there was not much more she was capable of giving. "I think you should hear me out first."

"Okay," he answered amiably. "Shoot."

She sat down on the opposite edge of the blanket. "We've been seeing a lot of each other the last few weeks—"

"Not as much as I'd like to, though," he interrupted her to say.

"Yes, well, that's what I'm trying to say." She continued hesitantly. "Maybe we should take things a bit slower."

Zachary frowned. "I don't understand."

"Our relationship has been developing too

74

quickly. I'd like to take some time and think it out."

"You mean, stop seeing each other," he said, anger plain in his voice and on his face.

"No," she replied quickly. "That's not . . . I don't want that to happen." She cast her gaze down to her hands, clasped tightly in her lap, cursing her indecision.

Zachary moved to sit beside her. "Then what do you want?" He lifted her chin with his finger till her eyes met his.

"I—I just don't want to jump into anything. I don't want to get too involved—"

"Too involved! Rachel, you're already involved, or at least I thought you were."

The sharpness in his voice cut her like a knife. "Zachary, please."

"Please what? Please take more time to convince myself of what I'm already sure of? Or take time to forget the feelings I have for you?"

"Don't!" she cried. "Don't do this! You just don't understand."

"I want to," he replied tenderly.

She looked into his warm eyes, her heart sinking. She was so confused she felt like crying. What could she tell him? What could she possibly say that would change the way things were? It wouldn't be easy to pour out the whole story, even though she knew what his immediate reaction would be. He would say that children didn't matter to him, that all that mattered was their love. But sometime, somewhere down the road, he would regret it, and she wasn't going to be the cause of anyone's regret again.

"Rachel?" he prompted softly.

She had to decide whether to take a chance or risk losing him altogether. "You know you're too impetuous, Zachary." She admonished him lightly, trying to put the old banter back in their conversation. "All I'm asking is that you give me some time. Let's just cool off the . . . physical side of our relationship for a while."

Zachary stared at her in disbelief. Then his expression turned dark and forbidding. "It's time we were getting back," he stated flatly. He started to gather up their things, his movements controlled and angry. He didn't seem to notice that Rachel wasn't helping. She couldn't. Tears were blurring her eyes.

CHAPTER FIVE

Zachary awoke with a start when his plane touched down at Houston's Hobby Airport. The feeling of being airborne one moment and on solid ground the next always disconcerted him. He supposed he should have gotten used to it by now, flying as often as he did, but he hadn't.

He stretched and yawned, then, rounding up his coat and briefcase, joined the line of passengers filing off the plane. There were other businessmen and businesswomen, camera-laden tourists, and a group of evangelical ministers ahead of him, so he patiently waited his turn to be ushered off by the smiling stewardess at the door.

"Did you have a nice flight?" she asked.

Zachary shrugged into his coat and grinned. "I believe if God had intended man to fly

. . ." He let the cliché trail over his shoulder as he moved down the gangway into the crowded airport.

Like the seasoned traveler he was, he claimed his suitcase quickly and ran through the airport and into a steamy Houston drizzle to a waiting taxi. He gave his office address to the driver and settled back with a sigh.

This trip to Corpus Christi had been fairly routine, with the exception of an unexpected bureaucratic tangle over an oil lease which delayed his departure several days. As a result, a week had passed since he had last seen Rachel at the picnic. They had driven home in silence and finished their discussion at Zachary's house, once he had calmed down enough to speak.

She said she wanted some sort of sexual cooling-off period to give her time to think, but she refused to explain her behavior fully. He thought the idea absurd and said so. In the shouting match that ensued, he found himself telling her angrily he would have to think it over. Then Rachel had left, brown hair swirling and an angry set to her jaw. The next day he was called to Corpus Christi on business. Though he had fully intended to let tempers cool for a few days, he hadn't meant to be gone so long. But perhaps it was for the best, he thought.

Zachary stared out the cab window as they circled the inner city on the six-ten loop. He tried for what felt like the millionth time to piece together what had gone wrong. Admittedly his relationship with Rachel seemed from the very beginning somehow unreal and dreamlike. She was perfect for him, or as near as he ever wanted to come. He thought she felt the same way, was certain of it—or at least he had been. Her sudden about-face left him feeling disoriented and more than a little bewildered.

What in heaven's name had come over her? True, they had gone from first meeting to spending the night together in record time, but that was because they had so much in common and were so intensely attracted to each other. If things had been moving fast, it was a pace they set by mutual need and consent, and they both had been comfortable with it until a week ago. Zachary wanted nothing more than for everything to continue as it had been, with one major difference. Zachary wanted Rachel for his own, forever. However, as tempting as the idea was, he could hardly carry her off and force her into wedlock.

Zachary chuckled and shook his head. "Maybe I'm getting my just desserts," he murmured under his breath.

"What's that?" the cabdriver asked, looking a bit uneasily in the rearview mirror.

"What? Oh, nothing. Just talking to myself."

The driver shrugged. "Whatever." He subtly increased his speed.

Zachary could hardly explain to the cabby what struck him as so ironic. When he thought about it, the whole situation was rather bizarre.

79

In his youth Zachary had been quite adept at sensing when a girl was getting too serious and at carefully disentangling himself. Now it seemed the same thing was happening again—in reverse. He was definitely serious about Rachel, he wanted her as his wife, but just when he was about to ask the question, she started talking about "slowing down and cooling off," definitely words from his past.

There was, however, a very significant difference. When he had said things like that, it had been as an overture to separation. Rachel didn't want that; at least she had told him she didn't last week. But even if she hadn't, he still knew instinctively that separation was the farthest thing from her mind—for the moment at least. So what did she want? Her reluctance to explain her reasons to him left Zachary baffled. He did know one thing, though: She was far too involved to back out now.

The answer to his problem was on his desk along with his other mail when he got to his office. He rubbed his hands and laughed with glee. Now if only he could charm Rachel into rising to the bait.

"About time you showed up," Martin said disdainfully when he saw Zachary. "That Triumph you bought at auction is starting to depress the other cars. I had to quarantine it out back."

Zachary laughed. "You mean you aren't working on it?"

Martin almost shivered. "It's all yours, friend, and good luck."

When Zachary formulated his plans for Rachel, he knew he was in for a fight, but he thought he could get the job done. Now, however, as Angela ushered him into the office and he saw Rachel, he had serious doubts. For his scheme to work, he would have to heat her up while he remained cool and aloof—or at least appeared to have given in to her demands to take things slowly. Yet the moment the door closed behind him he wanted to jump across the desk and show her how much he had missed her. With all the determination he possessed, he managed to force an unconcerned smile to his face. "Hi, Rachel. Sorry I haven't been by in a while, but I've been out of town."

Rachel nearly gasped at the sight of Zachary standing before her. In his absence her success, the nearly completed expansion of her business, everything seemed to have lost some of the shine they had had before their disagreement. Still, she had gone through such periods of adjustment before and had nearly convinced herself this was just one more. It surprised and excited her to see him again, but what really surprised her was the feeling of relief that washed over her. He hadn't walked out of her life forever!

"Zachary! I—I'm glad you're here." That was the understatement of the year. She tried to calm herself when all she really wanted to do was jump up and run into his arms, feel his lips pressed against hers, his hands . . . *Stop it.* She chided herself. *You need time to think, and those kinds of thoughts aren't on the agenda.*

"Oh?" He didn't know what he expected to hear, but that wasn't it.

"Yes. Martin's been pestering me about that Triumph of yours." *Please,* she thought. *Please don't come any closer!*

Zachary walked over to her and sat down in front of her desk, wondering at the wild look in her eyes as he did so. "I'm having it towed home tomorrow. It's one of the reasons I'm here," he said as casually as he could manage with her so near.

She cleared her throat nervously. "One of ?" Her hands started to fuss with the neckline of her silk blouse, but she stopped herself before he noticed.

"Yes. I have a proposal for you."

"Zachary, I thought I explained—"

"You didn't explain anything." He interrupted her a bit more sharply than he intended. He cautioned himself to calm down. "But that's not the kind of proposal I meant." Zachary took from his pocket the flyer he had found on his desk and handed it to her. Their hands touched, and it was all he could do to keep from grabbing her.

Dammit, Rachel thought as she tried to concentrate on the paper in front of her. *One more overreaction like that, and he'll sense my indeci-*

sion and pounce on it. Her hands shook slightly with the effort of holding her emotions in check, so she put the flyer on her desk and read it with her hands clasped tightly in her lap.

It was an advertisement inviting Zachary and the navigator of his choice to participate in a three-day antique car rally. Rachel felt the muscles of her stomach tighten slightly. "So?" she asked.

"So, I want you to be my map reader. I've done some racing in the past, so the driving isn't anything new to me, but going around in a circle is a lot different from negotiating the back roads of the Texas countryside. I can't think of anyone I'd rather spend three days and nights with in such close quarters."

Nights? Close quarters? "Now just a minute . . ."

Zachary held up his hand. "Calm down. I've decided you were right. We should give ourselves a cooling-off period."

Rachel looked startled. "You have?"

"Yes. The only thing that will be going fast in this rally are the cars, and since we have to use back roads through small towns and a speeding ticket means disqualification, it looks like a sedate and thoroughly enjoyable way to give ourselves that time." He smiled reassuringly. "We'll be using the MG, that's what I meant by close quarters, and some of the checkpoints on the prescribed route are overnight stopovers. The rally will probably draw quite a crowd, so there'll be plenty of people around."

He knew he was making it sound as if she didn't trust him or her own resolve. "I don't need supervision to keep to our bargain," Rachel said coolly.

"Neither do I," he assured her. He did, however, have some plans for those overnight stopovers.

His expression and his words were convincing enough, but there was something . . . something in his eyes. "I'm really much too busy, Zachary. I've got the grand opening coming up, you know."

"It's only three days and nights, Rachel, and over the weekend at that. Think of what a great advertisement it would be to win and display the trophy at the opening."

He had a point, and a good one, damn him. She just wished he would quit mentioning nights. "Well, I don't know."

"Don't trust yourself around me, huh?" he asked with an infuriating grin.

"You needn't concern yourself with me," she replied airily. "I can take care of myself." She looked at him seriously, a nervous kind of excitement gnawing at her. "Do you think we could win?"

Zachary fought a smile of victory. He had her now. She was hooked by her own competitive spirit. "I do," he said honestly. "All the cars entered have to be at least three decades old; some

84

of the people I've talked to will be wearing period clothing. It promises to be an eccentric rally."

"You should feel right at home," Rachel quipped sardonically.

Zachary ignored her. "Most of the entrants will be more interested in showing off their exotic cars and clothes than in taking first place. I think we have an excellent chance to win if we take it seriously. Rallying is what the MG was built for."

Rachel was becoming more excited by the minute. "I intend to take it very seriously." She stood up, slapping her palm on her desk in emphasis. "You've got yourself a navigator."

Zachary rose with her, feeling her excitement spread to him as if it were contagious. It surprised him to realize that he, too, planned to take the rally seriously. Of course, there would still be plenty of time for other things.

Rachel came around the desk and offered him her hand to shake on the partnership. She regretted the action as soon as her skin touched his. He pulled her close, unable to resist her for another instant. "We've come too far to seal our deals with handshakes, Rachel," he murmured before crushing his lips against hers.

Rachel felt a familiar fire consuming her as Zachary's arms closed around her. The tips of her breasts made her exquisitely aware of the warmth of his body as he pressed her against his hard, lean form. Then, just as her hands began wandering to the back of his neck, he released her.

"I'll keep my part of the bargain, sweet Rachel," he said in a voice that was strained and hoarse.

She stepped away, her throat feeling tight. "Yes, well, I—I suppose I'd better try to round up some maps. We'll need every advantage we can get," she said, unable to look at him.

"I'll be in touch."

After he had gone, and Rachel's throbbing senses had returned to nearly normal, she began to have doubts. It appeared Zachary was indeed going to stick to his end of the bargain as best he could, and it also appeared he might be better at it than she was. *Oh, God! What have I gotten myself into?* she wondered morosely.

CHAPTER SIX

The large circular drive of the rallymaster's home was lined with gleaming vintage autos, and the vast front porch of his colonial-style house was surrounded by a large crowd of people. This was indeed an eccentric group, Rachel mused as she looked around.

On the tree-shaded lawn was an excited group of people who, Rachel realized, were their competition. Some, as Zachary had foretold, had come in period clothing. There were hoop skirts and bow ties, Barney Oldfield-style dusters and goggles, full-cut suits and old-fashioned fedoras. Rachel was sure she was infinitely more comfortable in her jeans and top than they were on this sunny day.

Zachary was similarly attired. His only

concession to race day was an abused-looking tweed cap tilted rakishly on his head.

"What," Rachel had asked when she first saw the cap, "is that?"

"My lucky hat," he replied.

"If you say so."

"It is lucky, Rachel. We couldn't win without it."

"If you say it's a hat, I'll have to believe you, but it looks more like something that crawled on your head and fell asleep."

The rallymaster—in charge of everything from planning the route and checkpoints to making sure the winning team's final times were correct—obviously took his job very seriously. He was now standing in front of the group and regaling them with a history of the automobile rally.

"In the early days of the automobile," the impeccably dressed gentleman began, "groups of wealthy enthusiasts would gather together and talk about their adventures with their new, expensive toys." He looked around to make sure he had everyone's attention before he continued. "The gathering spot was usually the local pub, the discussions usually about how quickly and dependably a particular automobile could go from here to there."

Rachel noticed several people fidgeting, anxious to get on with the race. She was one of them.

"One thing led to another. A route which included several of these gatherings or rallying spots was agreed upon, timed checkpoints were set up to keep everyone honest, and the sport of automobile rallying was born." The rallymaster looked at the contestants and smiled.

"Uh-oh," Zachary whispered. "Here it comes."

"As you can imagine, with all those people racing around from pub to pub, those old-time rallies could get pretty lively!" He waited while the crowd laughed appreciatively, then appeared to be winding down. "Our rally, however, will have checkpoints only where you must stop to get your cards marked with place and time, though there will be beverages available at the overnight stopovers," he said with a wink. "If all goes well, we plan to make this an annual event, an event which harks back to those early days when inventive navigation, creative map reading, and on-the-spot mechanical skills meant more than speed and death-defying maneuvers. Good luck!"

They all applauded, more because he had stopped speaking than anything else.

Rachel edged closer to Zachary. " 'Harks back'?"

"I think he's running for public office next spring."

When they all had gotten their materials and assured the officials they understood the rules, the teams took off one by one in timed intervals, and the race was on.

Rachel was at first much too busy reading maps and too excited by the competition to be overly concerned about the close quarters in the MG. As she gained confidence in her navigational abilities, however, Zachary's masculine presence became all too noticeable. The day grew warm, even with the wind rushing by them in the convertible sports car, and Zachary peeled off his shirt; his tanned skin glistened in the bright sunlight. It was all she could do to concentrate on the road.

The cars nearest them, much more elderly than Zachary's and not designed for the twisting country road, soon dropped far behind, leaving them purring along alone in the MG. Then Zachary's hat blew off.

"What are you doing?" Rachel asked in alarm as he slowed down.

"I lost my hat."

"But we can't afford the time! I'll buy you a new one."

"I told you, it's lucky. Besides, it might get run over."

"Probably do it some good. It certainly couldn't hurt it," Rachel said, fuming.

Without warning the engine of the MG sputtered and died as Zachary pulled off the road to turn around. "Damn!"

"You turn the engine on right now!" Rachel cried.

"I didn't turn it off. Something's wrong."

She looked at him skeptically while he tried to

start the car, but it would run only a few seconds before dying again. "You and that damn lucky hat! What's wrong?"

"Fuse, I think. Let me see." He leaned across her and checked the fuse box, the sun-warmed skin of his back mere inches from her face. He rubbed against her breasts, and she began to doubt there was anything wrong with the car at all. Zachary was probably just up to his old tricks again.

His position got even more intimate as he searched for something in the glove compartment, balancing himself with his hand on the seat between her legs. Slowly but surely his hand slipped further between her jean-clad thighs, moving to within inches of her femininity. "Zachary . . ." she warned.

"Oh, excuse me," he said, and moved his hand to the edge of the seat as he continued searching through the cluttered glove box. "I could have sworn I left those extra fuses in here," he muttered, ignoring Rachel's growing unease at having him practically on top of her. "Ah, here they are."

Now his head was in her lap as he fiddled with the fuse box underneath the dash. Her thighs were growing warm from the heat of his body as he pressed intimately against her. Damn Zachary! She knew he was doing this on purpose, trying to make her aware of her own desires and his as well.

And he was succeeding, in spite of her best

efforts to ignore the warmth spreading over her. The broad shoulders resting against her thighs, his head pressing firmly into her belly as he changed positions. "Zachary, I think it would be better if I just get out of the car while you work. I'm obviously in the way."

"Oh, that's okay. This really isn't uncomfortable for me at all," he told her, brushing against her breasts again.

Maybe not for you, she thought sarcastically. She was beginning to think this trip might not be such a good idea after all, not if Zachary was going to tease her at every turn. But she couldn't turn back now and would just have to stay out of his reach as best she could. "Tell you what," she said as she quickly extricated herself from under him. "I'll go look for your hat while you fix the car." She stood up and walked back, found his hat at the side of the road, and was returning when she heard the MG purr to life. Zachary picked her up, turned the car around, and they were on their way again. The cool breeze felt wonderful. The day had suddenly gotten much warmer.

When they passed through the last checkpoint of the day and arrived at the motor inn where the teams were to stay for the night, the sun was already going down. They checked into their rooms—separate rooms, she noticed with relief—showered, and had a pleasant dinner at a nearby restaurant. The other teams were there as well, and they had a drink in the bar while discussing the day's adventures. A couple of teams had had to drop out because of mechanical problems. As predicted, others were mainly along for the fun of it and were not serious competition. Rachel and Zachary returned to their rooms filled with the exciting knowledge that they were one of the top three teams.

Rachel just barely avoided falling under Zachary's spell when he kissed her good night. Reluctantly she pulled free of his grasp and locked the door to her room, though to keep him out or herself in she didn't know. She sat on her bed, her thoughts a mixture of excitement and sensuality. The smell of Zachary's sun-warmed skin, the sinewy movement of his muscles as he confidently drove the MG were strong in her memory. Her body fairly ached with sexual tension. She knew she must not let her desires—or Zachary's—interfere with the object of this cooling-off period. She was glad to be with him, but she had to think.

She was stuck, she thought, trapped in a vicious circle of needing to be with Zachary but certain he would never settle for continuing their relationship on a less serious basis. As she continued to torment herself, she slipped out of her clothes and into a cool, filmy nightgown. A knock on her door startled her from her reverie.

"Rachel? It's Zachary."

"What do you want?" she asked warily. She hadn't thought to bring a robe. Her nightgown covered her but was thin and clingy and displayed a lush amount of cleavage.

"I need help," he answered.

She knew she shouldn't open the door dressed as she was, but the pained tone in his voice compelled her to do so.

Zachary, barefoot and clad only in a pair of brief gym shorts, came through the door and thrust a bottle of lotion into her hand. "I managed to sunburn my shoulders," he said, closing the door behind him. His eyes roved over her slowly. "Expecting me to drop by?" he asked, desire beginning to smolder in his eyes.

"I was just going to go to bed," she explained, crossing her arms over her breasts.

Zachary's eyebrows arched. "Sounds inviting."

"That was not," she answered, prodding him until he turned his back to her, "an invitation." She looked at his red shoulders. "My, you did get a burn. Sit on the bed so I can reach you."

He did as directed, wincing slightly when she squirted the soothing lotion on his neck and shoulders and gently rubbed it in. "Well, here I am, in your bedroom, on your bed. Give you any ideas?" he asked.

Rachel laughed at the hopeful tone in his voice. "No," she said firmly. What was giving her ideas was the smooth, slick feel of his skin as she tenderly applied the lotion. The muscles of his shoulders felt powerful and strong. She found herself rubbing a larger and larger area,

94

running her hands down his back, along his sides and the ridge of his spine to the edge of his shorts. Her breathing increased slightly.

"Mmm. That's delicious." He grabbed her hands and pulled her down to sit in his lap. "Shall I return the favor?" Before she could answer, he squirted some of the lotion on her shoulders between the deep scoop back of the nightgown, causing her to shiver at its coolness. Then his warm hands blended it into her skin. She found herself shivering again, this time for an entirely different reason.

"Zachary," she moaned as he slipped off the straps to reach more of her silky skin, "I think that's enough."

He turned her head and kissed her softly on the lips. She held her nightgown up by pressing her hands to her chest, struggling to rise away from him. His kiss became more insistent, demanding, making her aware of his desire, as did the hardness beneath her. Just as she was about to succumb to her own desires, he pulled the straps of her gown back onto her shoulders and released her. "I suppose you're right," he said huskily. He got up and went to the door, leaving her standing by the bed. "See you tomorrow, bright and early."

When she could finally trust her weakened legs to support her, Rachel locked the door after him and leaned against it, her senses reeling. "That was close," she muttered under her breath. Somehow she felt instinctively that before this trip was over, there would be even closer calls. She didn't know if she could stand up under Zachary's constant masculine presence. She climbed gratefully into bed and tried to sleep, but it was quite a while before the erotic images in her mind allowed her to close her eyes.

The next day's rallying went extremely well, with more teams dropping out, victims of the brutal Texas sun. The MG purred along without complaint, Rachel thanking Providence for Zachary's tender shoulders—he kept his shirt on, sparing her the tempting sight of his tanned torso.

By afternoon they had secured third place, then moved into second when the doctor who held that honor before them was called away for a gallbladder operation. Again they pulled into a stylish motel for the night, washed off the day's dust, and went to dinner with the remaining teams.

"I've just been sitting in the car all day," Rachel remarked over her large portion of fresh seafood. "I can't understand why I'm so hungry."

Zachary smiled at her, his dark eyes fairly devouring her in her white silk dress. He, too, had a good appetite. "I heard somewhere that riding in a car does burn a few calories every hour. Maybe that amount increases when you're winning a race."

"We're only in second place," she said, cautioning him.

"We'll make it to first tomorrow. I can feel it in my bones."

Rachel shifted in her chair. "I can feel it, too, but not in my bones. That MG isn't the smoothest-riding car in the world."

Zachary's eyes brightened. "I know the cure for that."

"Oh?"

"You take a hot bath, then lay facedown on the bed while I massage—"

"I think I'll be fine by tomorrow," Rachel interrupted him to say. All she needed to push her over the edge was Zachary's strong fingers massaging the sore muscles of her buttocks.

He looked disappointed, ate a bit of his lobster, then smiled warmly. "Okay. Maybe some exercise would help. I hear there's a good band in the lounge. Why don't we join the crowd and dance for a while?"

"You never give up, do you?"

"Me?" he asked innocently.

"Yes, you. First you suggest a—a suggestive massage, and I hesitate to think what you might suggest on the dance floor."

Zachary tried to keep a straight face, but an extremely risqué grin kept breaking through. "Me?" he repeated in an offended tone. "Me?"

Rachel had to laugh at his fight to keep his expression innocent. What harm could a few dances in a public lounge do? "All right."

The band was good, playing popular tunes softly and slowly, but Rachel could hardly call the atmosphere public. Even after her eyes had adjusted, the dance floor seemed barely lighted, and the dim lounge was cozy and intimate.

As they danced, Zachary's body moved rhythmically against hers, causing a warm glow to spread through her body. As when they made love, he seemed in constant touch with her feelings, making her all too aware of how well suited they were to each other. Indeed, dancing with Zachary was very much like making love. His powerful thighs against hers, his strong arms enfolding her, pressing her tightly against him, the soothing and sensual movements of his hands stroking her spine. He tilted his head and kissed her softly, his tongue teasing her lips before plunging between them. He tasted pleasantly of coffee and the brandy they had had after dinner.

Rachel moaned, very softly, her body weak with the rush of pleasurable sensations. Their lips parted, and she looked into his eyes, alive with a desire just barely held in check. She, too, fought the desire Zachary had brought boiling to the surface. "Zachary . . ."

"Would you like to go back to the motel?" he asked.

She knew exactly what he was asking. Though she fought against the impulse, she found herself saying, "Yes."

They walked arm in arm to Rachel's room. The darkened breezeway was warm with a humid wind from the south. The smell of open fields and growing plants intermingled with a touch of the sea from the Gulf of Mexico.

"Sweet Rachel," Zachary murmured before taking total possession of her lips again. Away from prying eyes, shrouded in the dark, his kiss was much deeper, his hands more bold. He caressed her breasts through the thin fabric of her silk dress until she moaned with suppressed need. "I don't know how much longer I can resist you, sweet Rachel. Every day I feel you close to me, smell your nearness. I—"

"Please," Rachel whispered, putting her fingers to his lips. "I know how you feel. Believe me, I really do. But there are so many questions in my mind, so much you don't know."

"Tell me," he demanded softly. "I want to know everything about you."

The mere thought of telling Zachary everything was so inviting yet so treacherous. He wouldn't lie to her, she knew that. Her hard years of growing up had taught her how to judge character extremely well. But eventually a man like him would have regrets about committing himself to a woman who couldn't have children —a barren woman. Tears formed in her eyes. At least she had a career, that safe territory she had fallen back on for so many years. She forced herself to think about her business—the expansion, the good publicity of winning this rally. "We have to get up early tomorrow, Zachary. Good night."

"Why are you crying? Wait—"

Rachel closed the door on him and fell on her bed, crying, ignoring his urgent knock. Eventually he went away, and she undressed for bed, sleeping no better than she had the previous night.

There was a growing excitement, an urgent feeling in the air the next day that overwhelmed any thoughts of the previous night's confrontation. Today was the final day. The fight for first place had come down to two teams, with Zachary and Rachel in the lead one moment, behind the next. Though Zachary felt pressed to break the rules and exceed the posted speed limit, his strong will held him back, and his discipline eventually won the contest. They passed through the last checkpoint to the accompaniment of much fanfare and congratulations. Their time for the entire rally was only seconds behind their highly competitive adversary's, but that team had been observed speeding, thus disqualifying themselves.

A dizzying rush of applause, handshaking, and awards ceremonies followed, along with several toasts to the winners in the local pub. Rachel and Zachary drank in the adulation with aplomb —and fatigue. They had been fighting not only the clock for three days but their own desires as well.

Finally, trophy in hand, they made their way to the lovely seaside inn that was to be their last stopover before heading home. When Rachel entered her room, however, all her happiness dissolved.

She looked again at the king-size bed before returning her accusing gaze to Zachary. "Just what are you up to?" she demanded.

"I don't know what you mean, Rachel. Is something wrong?" he asked, his face totally innocent.

His feigned innocence only angered her more. "We have only one room and one bed, unless you have another one hidden somewhere," she said sarcastically. She was hot, tired, hungry, and desperately in need of a bath. The MG didn't have air conditioning, of course, and the Texas sun had been unbearably hot today. The last thing she needed right now was to argue with Zachary.

"No, one room and one king-size bed were all that was available," he responded. He moved about the room, unpacking. "Did you want to shower first, or shall I go ahead of you?"

"I'll go first," she snapped.

"Then I'll just bring in the rest of the luggage while you're bathing, dear," he said, turning on his heel.

"Zachary, damn you . . ." she yelled at his retreating back. "Oh, blast," she muttered, grabbing her toiletry bag viciously and heading for the bathroom.

As she showered and bathed, her temper cooled down a little. She should have known what to expect from Zachary. He still wanted

101

her, desired her openly, and was doing everything possible to make her aware of her own
desires toward him. A knock on the door interrupted her thoughts, and the virile man who
filled them walked in without asking. "Zachary!" she exclaimed.

"Rachel . . ." he started to say at the same
time. His eyes seemed to devour her, his words
forgotten.

"Did you want something?" she asked from
the tub, regretting the words before the sen-
tence was finished.

"What are you willing to give me?" he murmured huskily, his gaze continuing to rove over
her fine body. Her breasts glistened with drops
of water, taut and lush, her skin reddened slightly from sun and scrubbing.

Rachel's hands fluttered delicately to cover
herself as she opened her mouth to speak, but no
words came. For a moment, by the look in his
eyes, she thought he might jump into the bath-
tub with her.

He ached to reach out and run his fingers
across her moist and supple skin, to feel it come
alive beneath his touch as it had so readily in the
past, to feel her muscles contract around him,
holding him tightly to her. *Stop yourself*, he
thought. *You've got to stay in control.* "I wanted
to know if you were willing to have dinner with
the others or if you wanted to eat alone, with
just me for company?" he quipped, already
knowing her answer.

"Dinner with the others, thank you." She could feel his eyes taking in the sight of her, his gaze so intense she felt as if he were touching her, stroking her to awareness. "I—I'm almost done in here," she added, willing him to leave.

"No hurry. The others—and I—can wait," he told her as he retreated and closed the door.

Rachel breathed a sigh of relief, then hurriedly completed her bath.

Later, giddy from the wine and the congratulations of the losing teams, Rachel took Zachary's arm, and they returned to their room. Their room! She had almost forgotten. Forcibly she quieted a rising sense of panic, deciding she was being silly.

Rachel, she told herself as he opened the door, *you are a mature, grown, confident woman. You've slept with this man before, so what's the problem with simply sharing this room? It isn't as if you didn't know each other intimately.* That, she realized, was the problem. Even if she could trust Zachary—and he had shown every indication that she could—could she trust herself? "I don't think this is going to work, Zachary."

"Rachel, I don't see any problem. This bed is big enough for four, let alone two," he said, trying to remain calm. As they busied themselves getting ready for bed, she began dragging her feet, even spending some time locked in the bathroom. He was just about at wits' end.

"You could at least offer to sleep on the floor or in one of the chairs," she pointed out angrily.

He shook his head. "Not me. I don't mind sleeping in the same bed with you."

Drat the man! He wasn't even trying to take her seriously. "Zachary—"

"What's wrong, Rachel?" he said tauntingly. "Are you afraid you won't be able to resist my golden body?" His voice held a teasing quality, but he watched her carefully.

"Think a lot of yourself, don't you?" she exclaimed.

"No more than you do," he returned just as quickly. "It's nice to know how irresistible I am, though. I'm sure I can find someone who wants me," he added with a heavy sigh.

Rachel's face tightened. "Zachary, this has nothing to do with our problem." He was right. He wouldn't have any trouble finding someone else.

Zachary patted the bed with an elaborate gesture. "I thought this was our problem, sweet Rachel."

"And don't call me that!"

"Well, it is true you aren't being very sweet right now, but I forgive you."

"Look, Zachary, I'm tired, and I want to go to sleep."

He threw up his hands. "Go right ahead! I'm not stopping you." He looked at her, his eyes sparkling with enjoyment as she moved toward the bed. The lamp behind her clearly revealed

104

her long limbs and firm breasts through her nightgown. "I want to assure you, though," he murmured, "I *am* looking."

"Oh!" Rachel hurriedly threw back the covers and climbed in. He didn't need to be any more aroused than he already was.

"Show's over, huh? I think you could have at least bounced around a little more since that's all I'm going to get tonight," he said complainingly.

He really was outrageous! "You're right, the show is over." She turned out the lamp. She wasn't about to tell him to go to bed; he would only take the order as an invitation. "Good night, Zachary."

"Good night, Rachel," he replied softly as he climbed into bed beside her. "And I want you to know if you just can't resist me, I'm ready, willing, and able," he whispered. He moved a little closer to her. "I'd even let you stop at just a kiss if you wanted," he added persuasively.

Rachel smiled warmly in the dark but kept her voice firm. "Good night, Zachary." As outrageous and exciting as he was, there was still something comforting about having him so close. She soon fell into a deep sleep.

Zachary awoke to find his body entangled with hers. She was sleeping peacefully, and her even breathing was deep and slow. God, she was a beautiful woman! And not just physically—her mind was bright and clear, and her soul was full of beauty, too. He lay there watching her sleep, wanting her. But he could wait. Eventually she would trust him enough to tell him what the problem was. Till then he would accept what was between them. That did not mean, however, that he was going to sit back and wait for the problem to come out in the open. He would keep pushing because the sooner he knew what was wrong, the faster they could be married. And he was going to marry Rachel. He intended to love, cherish, and possess her forever. He wanted to take care of her, to love and laugh and even cry with her. To wipe away the hurt and tears and see her laughing again. She was the one he had waited for all his life, and nothing was going to stand in his way now.

Rachel stirred in her sleep, moving closer to his warm body. Unconsciously she wrapped her hand around his firm waist. She sighed, then slowly realized what she was doing in her half-sleeping state. The last thing she wanted at the moment was to be a tease. She wondered how she was going to remove her body from his without awakening him.

Her nightgown had ridden high on her thighs as their legs intertwined, his hairy and strong, hers smooth and silky. Her head was snuggled into his throat and rested against his broad tanned chest. He really did have a golden body —tan all over. *Rachel,* she told herself silently and sternly, *stop! You aren't solving any problems thinking this way, only creating more.*

106

Zachary wasn't sure how long he could remain unresponsive to her. Her touch was driving him wild, causing a burning ache only she could relieve. If she moved her thigh any higher, she would be readily aware of how much he wanted her. He wasn't sure if he could stop himself then from arousing her as fully as she had him.

She heard Zachary's breathing change and knew he was awake. Disentangling her legs, she turned to look up at him. Barely suppressed desire smoldered in his black eyes as they gazed at her. Was desire reflected in her own?

"Do I at least get one good morning kiss?" he whispered sensually before taking possession of her mouth. His lips moved softly against hers, coaxing her mouth to open to his. Their tongues touched and darted away when his alarm watch chose that moment to go off.

"Saved by the alarm," she said huskily as their lips reluctantly parted.

"I didn't want to be saved." He groaned. He buried his head in her luxurious dark hair before drawing away hesitantly. Then he bounded out of bed before his baser instincts took over.

Rachel watched his sleek body as he walked to the bathroom and closed the door behind him. She sighed. Cooling-off period indeed! This whole trip had done little more than heighten her awareness of him, of her nearly uncontrollable desires. She was the one who wanted to slow down and think things out, wanted to do so without his powerful sensuality clouding her mind, but now she knew that just wasn't possible. She could be either with him—totally—or not at all, and now she wished only to return to the way things had been. Her body ached for him, but to give in now would only reinforce his belief that she couldn't live without him, and that would be a mistake. She still had a great deal to tell him.

Climbing out of the warm bed, Rachel felt a mixture of fear and excitement as she realized the trip had indeed served a purpose—his purpose, but no matter. At last she could admit to herself that serious or not, she didn't want to live without Zachary. But the realization was not an easy one, and it scared her to dwell too long on what lay in store for them now. She could still lose him, but now she at last knew in her heart she had something to lose.

CHAPTER SEVEN

It was noon by the time they arrived at Zachary's house, where Rachel had left her car. The trip back had been pleasant enough, but she felt irritable and tense. Zachary seemed in a similar condition, and she knew why. The sexual tension seemed to arc between them like electricity flowing from two oppositely charged electrodes.

Zachary was well aware of her mood and the reason for it, but he knew it had to be Rachel who gave in first. The way he felt right now he could devour her in one delicious bite, but all he could do was continue to push her, a step at a time, back into his arms—and into his bed. "What's wrong?" he asked as he pulled the MG into the garage. "Hungry?" He put his hand on her thigh.

Hungry? She was ravenous! Not for food but for his touch. "Yes—no, oh, I don't know!" she snapped. She climbed out of the car and slammed the door, feeling as if she were running a fever. Her whole body felt hot.

Zachary grinned. "I know what you need, what we both need."

"You do?" Rachel ran the tip of her tongue across her lips to wet them. Her movement was unconsciously seductive.

"Um-hm," he murmured knowingly, grabbing their luggage and heading for the house.

Rachel followed, watching him carefully, a thrilling feeling in the pit of her stomach. He put the suitcases on his bed and turned to her, stepping closer. She felt herself drawn to him like a magnet. "What do we need?" she asked in a voice that was almost a whisper.

"Exercise," he said.

"Exercise?"

He nodded. "We've done nothing but ride in a car for three days, and I don't know about you, but except for last night," he said, his eyes twinkling, "I didn't sleep very well."

Now Rachel nodded, mesmerized, waiting for him to take her in his arms. She knew what kind of exercise she wanted. His hands, his lips, his tongue caressing her every curve, her muscles arching to meet his touch . . .

Zachary turned, opened his suitcase, and took out his gym shorts. "You can change here. I'll be waiting for you in the workout room." He left, closing the door behind him.

Rachel stood there for a moment in stunned silence, mouth agape, her mind grasping for meaning. Then an overwhelming fit of temper came over her. Zachary was no longer simply trying to tempt her; he was toying with her, using her passionate nature against her. "Damn you, Zachary!" she cried.

His muffled reply came through the closed door. "What?"

Rachel threw one of her shoes at the door, which it hit with a satisfying thump. "Dammit!"

"Are you all right, Rachel? What's going on in here?" He opened the door tentatively, his naked chest and inquiring grin infuriating her. She threw her other shoe, narrowly missing his head. He quickly closed the door again. "Oh, I see. Take your time. I'll start without you."

"Good idea," she muttered to herself. "The next time you want to make love, start without me!" She dressed in her exercise clothes, leotard and tights, trying to calm down. She had thought that throwing things was supposed to release your tensions, but somehow it seemed to have only increased them. Perhaps a good physical workout would help. She took several deep breaths and stretched to loosen her taut muscles, then went to join Zachary.

She had grown quite fond of exercising at his house. He had nearly everything her club had, except the crowds of primping, preening prima donnas. In his gym were weight machines, a stationary bicycle, exercise mat, and he even had a backyard pool and a sauna. As she rode the bike, her legs pumping furiously, some of her anger did drain away. Unfortunately, as her blood flowed through her veins and her breathing increased, her awareness of her sexual tensions also became more acute. Physical exercise often had an arousing effect on her, or at least made her more susceptible to arousal by generally increasing her feelings of good health and well-being.

A fine sheen of perspiration formed on Zachary's bare torso as he worked on the weight machine, his muscles flexing and relaxing rhythmically. He went from exercise to exercise, sometimes standing, other times sitting or lying on his back, and Rachel watched in fascination as the musculature of his arms, chest, and thighs became larger, more defined. His muscles worked easily, his breathing steady as he slowly and methodically went through the weight-lifting routine she had seen many times before.

But this time seemed different. This time there seemed something erotic about watching him. He was proud of his body, and he should be—he was in good shape for a man of thirty, let alone forty, virile, masculine, powerful. Rachel tore her eyes from him, her heart pounding from more than her workout. *Two can play at this game*, she thought.

112

She lay on the mat on the cool floor, doing trimming and toning exercises, a mixture of yoga and aerobics. She was proud of her body, too, lithe-limbed and supple; she could feel Zachary's eyes upon her like twin points of searing heat. She had meant to tease him, taunt him, but her plan backfired. Tension flowed over her, raising goose bumps on her damp skin. It was exciting and almost overpowering. She got to her feet, wrapping a towel around her neck. "I'm going to rinse off and swim for a while." She half walked, half ran from the room in an attempt to escape her own sensuality.

The water of the pool, though warmed by the sun, still felt cool and refreshing as she swam back and forth with leisurely strokes. Why had she taunted him like that? To get back at him because she imagined he was doing the same thing to her? She felt it went much deeper than that. Zachary had teased her unmercifully throughout the entire rally, pushing her to the limits of her control, while his strength of will seemed intact. It just wasn't fair! She wanted to see just how strong his iron will really was. Perhaps for the next few days she would turn the tables on him, push him to his limits for a change. She smiled mischievously.

Zachary jumped in, matching his stroke to hers, and they swam laps in the crystal water side by side for a while. "Hey!" he said at last, catching her by the ankle in the shallow end and pulling her beside him. "Let's take a breather."

"All right." She allowed him to pull her closer. Her skin felt slick and silky against his. Reaching up, she brushed drops of water from his face. "Too much for you?" she asked teasingly.

"I just got tired of chasing you." He pulled her even closer, pressing her against his slippery chest.

Rachel rubbed against him invitingly. "You've caught me. Now what?" she asked, her eyebrows arched in taunting query. He bent to kiss her, but she kicked away from him, trying to get to the side of the pool.

Zachary pulled her back into his embrace, running his hands down the back of her French-cut suit, molding her partially uncovered buttocks, and pressing her to his masculine hardness. "What are you up to, sweet Rachel?" he asked huskily. "Playing with fire?"

"Umm," she hummed noncommittally. She knew he could feel her hardened nipples against his chest. She pressed closer, swaying slightly in the water. "Just playing."

"Take care you don't get burned," he murmured. He lowered his head, his teeth nipped gently at the skin of her shoulders and neck before his tongue plunged between her partially opened lips. With a subtle movement he pulled the straps of her suit down and cupped her breasts in his hands, lifting and caressing, cherishing the feel of them against his palms. "Cold?" he asked softly.

Rachel moaned and moved away from him,

114

this time making it to the pool's edge. She pulled her suit up as she climbed from the water. "Yes. I'm going to take a sauna." Seductively, she walked away from him, feeling his eyes lingering on her.

The dry heat of the sauna felt marvelous after the quick cold shower Rachel took. She stretched out on her stomach, a towel between her and the hot redwood boards. Zachary joined her, cold drops of water from his shower falling onto her back as he bent to kiss her between the shoulder blades. His hands, cool and exciting, glided up her back, then over her shoulders and down again, taking the straps of her suit with them as he lightly caressed her sides, baring more of her slick skin to his hungry eyes.

"You should really be naked," he said huskily. "Allow your skin to breathe. Opens the pores."

Rachel turned her head slightly to look at him, startled to see he practiced what he preached. His brief suit had been replaced by a towel, wrapped carelessly around his waist. His strong tanned thighs and powerful chest glistened in the heat. "I see pores are not the only thing being naked in the sauna is good for," she said wickedly. "Your towel is opening up, too."

"Observant wench, aren't you?" he replied.

"Perhaps you had better take another cold shower."

"I have everything under control."

"Almost," she added for him. She would have to see what she could do about that, she thought.

He lay down on the bench above her, seemingly ignoring her, but she could feel his eyes on her back, now bare to the waist. With a graceful movement she swung her feet to the floor and sat up, pulled her suit the rest of the way off, then lay back down. She smiled with satisfaction at his quick intake of breath.

"You little tease!"

"I beg your pardon! You said I should let my skin breathe."

"It's breathing all right," he muttered under his breath. "And so am I—heavily."

"Excuse me?"

Zachary reached down and smoothed water from her shoulders, then her back, working his way down across her buttocks to her thighs. His touch felt as if his hands were charged with electricity, making her tingle all over. "There. Is your skin breathing nicely now?"

Rachel could barely reply, "F-fine, thank you." She gasped as his fingers continued to draw lazy patterns on her derriere. This wasn't quite working as planned. She had meant to arouse him past the point of no return and could instinctively feel she was close to doing just that. However, as his maddening touch stroked the backs of her thighs, she realized she was much closer to that point than he was. Her pulse raced in her ears; her breathing came in short gasps that sounded more like moans of pleasure with each passing second. If she didn't get out of here

116

—now—it would be she who pounced on him instead of the other way around.

Rachel sat up, struggling to rise and wrap her towel around her slippery form, but her movements were made sluggish by her desire and the heat. And then it was too late.

Zachary sat up with her and pulled her to him, her back against his hard stomach, her arms trapped to her sides by strong thighs. Slowly, teasingly, his hands slipped over her breasts, caressing and gliding until she was nearly incoherent. Enough was enough!

"If you don't carry me out of here, I'm going to seduce you right now," she whispered in a voice so hoarse she barely recognized it as her own.

"Too hot. We'd both expire," he cautioned her, even though his voice was full of desire.

"Watch me." Rachel turned and pressed against him, the silky feel of her body against his taut stomach making him groan. She felt light-headed when she stood up, her perspiration-slicked skin slipping against every inch of him until she cradled his face between her breasts.

"Oh, God, sweet Rachel." He swung her into his arms. "We're both about to pass out," he murmured as he carried her out of the sauna. The cool breeze felt wonderful against their flushed bodies. Zachary held her tightly to him as he slowly turned a warm shower to cool. Then, still dripping, he carried her into his bedroom, and they collapsed onto the bed.

Rachel's nipples were hard against his chest. He sipped at her lips, ravenous for the taste of her. They both knew that this time there would be no pulling back, and the knowledge filled them with sweet anticipation. Her legs trembled as she wrapped them around his taut form. They joined with an almost savage frenzy powered by their mutual desire. Every nerve, every fiber of Rachel's being seemed on fire and almost too sensitive. She writhed against Zachary in utter abandon, driving him wild. The explosive sensuality in his eyes as he looked into hers was intense—almost frightening.

But her passion was as strong as his. She wanted him, needed him, and he filled her completely. She was torn between wanting this feeling to go on and on and wanting release from the unbelievable tension of the last few days.

Zachary's intense lovemaking rapidly washed the dilemma from her mind. He reveled in her pleasure, devouring her, his mouth and hands and body making her his own. Finally they cried out together in a rare, dizzying moment of shared ecstasy. Exhausted, they napped in each other's arms, only to awake to make love again and again. Each time seemed stronger and more complete than the time before.

Eventually, with the shadows deepening around them, they decided to dress and eat, still exchanging intimate and lingering caresses. Zachary grilled steaks, made a crisp salad, and poured red wine. Then his mood and expression turned serious. It was a seriousness Rachel remembered well.

"Does this mean the cooling-off period is over?" he asked, his hand closing over hers.

"Zachary, I—I need more time," she began softly, only to have her words halted when he squeezed her hand.

"We complete each other, Rachel. We need each other. You can't deny that any longer."

She looked away from his penetrating gaze, her soul in turmoil, her mind made up. "No, I can't." She turned back to him and smiled hesitantly. "Even if you would let me."

"And I won't," he assured her. He returned her smile. "I'm not forcing you into anything; you know that as well as I do. I'm simply demanding that you face facts."

"I know. But there are things you don't know about me, things—"

Zachary put his fingers to her lips. "I'll know all about you soon enough, or at least as much as you want me to know," he said with a grin. "We'll have plenty of time."

She nodded soberly. "I suppose we will. You're right. The cooling-off period is over."

CHAPTER EIGHT

Dinner finished, Rachel and Zachary went out to his patio overlooking the pool. A full moon glimmered on the water's placid surface. In the dark, as they sat side by side, a closeness settled in around them. It was a time for intimacies and for secrets.

"How do you feel about long engagements, Rachel?" Zachary asked.

The question caught her off guard. Zachary was good at doing that to her—too good. Almost from the day they met Rachel felt as if she were perpetually unsure of her footing. "I—I think they are a very good idea."

"So do I. Especially in our case." He turned to her, the moonlight reflected in his eyes. "Will you marry me?"

Oh, God! "Zachary, you're doing it again," she said, cautioning him.

"What?"

"Pushing too hard. You quite eloquently showed me the error of my ways with the so-called cooling-off period. But I still need time to think."

One way or another he was determined to pin her down. He wasn't about to lose her now. "That's what I'm asking, what I'm trying to give you," he explained. "Isn't an engagement supposed to be a time of deciding what to do?"

"I suppose, but—"

"Then will you at least agree to think about it?"

Rachel sighed. Persuasive bastard! "I'm beginning to understand your success in business, Zachary, but I have some experience in this area myself, and I will not be railroaded."

Zachary threw his hands up. "For heaven's sake, Rachel, I'm not railroading you! I'm only suggesting an engagement. I'm hardly the type to drag you off to a justice of the peace in the middle of the night," he said in an exasperated tone.

She wouldn't bet on it. "All right, all right. Yes."

"Yes, you'll marry me or yes, you'll think about it?"

Rachel had to laugh. "Yes, I'll think about it."

A small enough amount of progress, but one with big implications. He would accept it for now. "Good. That's all I ask." He got up and disappeared into the house for a moment. When he returned, he handed her a small velvet-covered box.

Hands trembling, Rachel opened the hinged lid, knowing what she would find. Still, a gasp escaped her lips. Nestled in the box was a sparkling emerald in an antique gold filigree setting. "Zachary," she said, stunned, "it's lovely."

"Do you accept it?" he asked, his inquiring eyes watching her every move and expression.

She met his black eyes, her gaze roving over his chiseled, handsome face. "I do accept it, but —"

"But?"

Rachel turned from those searching eyes. "You have a right to know certain things. Things which could . . . change your opinion of me."

There was a despairing quality to her voice which touched him deeply. "Nothing could do that, Rachel. I know you were married before. I know you had an unpleasant divorce. None of that and nothing else changes the way I feel."

"Please," she said quickly, standing up and walking slowly to the edge of the pool, "don't say any more. Not yet. Hear me out first."

A moment passed while Rachel collected her thoughts, deciding how to proceed. Finally she began in a weak voice. "How do you feel about children, Zachary?"

"Oh, Rachel, it's much too soon to—"

"No!" She interrupted him, her voice sharper

than intended, but she had to know. "This is very important to me." She looked at him, her expression emphasizing her words, then turned back to stare into the water. Her hand unconsciously squeezed the box containing the ring. "Do you want children?"

Zachary looked at her back, puzzled. "I've never really thought much about it, Rachel." He shrugged. "I suppose that says something about how I feel. Children have never been important to me."

"Was marriage?" she asked.

"Well, no, but—"

"Then how do you know?"

"Rachel, what does all this have to do with marrying me?"

"Everything," she answered quietly. She supposed his answer was as much as she could expect. Certainly, from this point on, it was as much as she could believe without some doubt creeping in. "As I said, you have a right to know." She took a deep breath. She thought that when the time came, telling Zachary about her problem would be easy. It wasn't. "Bill and I, our divorce . . ." Again she turned to look at him. His eyes were puzzled and concerned.

"Go on," he said softly, sensing when to push and when to back off.

"You may have the impression we separated because we weren't compatible, and while that is certainly true, it's not the whole story. Bill divorced me, because I—I couldn't give him children." Rachel held her breath.

Zachary still looked puzzled. "I don't understand."

"It's just that I, well, I have a fertility problem. Bill and I couldn't have children no matter how hard we tried."

"Rachel," he said, his eyebrows arched, "perhaps I'm stating the obvious, but it could have been Bill's problem, not yours."

She waved aside the comment. "He saw a doctor. Besides, he has two children now by his second wife."

"I see. And you? Did you see a doctor?"

"Yes."

There was a strong note of finality in Rachel's voice. The matter was closed, and Zachary would leave it that way. He saw the pain and fear in her eyes and wanted only to wash it all away, leaving just happiness in its place. He stood and went to her side, then lifted her chin with his finger until her eyes met his. "Did you think that would change anything, Rachel? Did you really think I would consider you unfit to be my wife?" She nodded hesitantly, and Zachary closed his arms around her, pulled her close, and kissed her gently on the forehead. "I want you, Rachel, not children." He pulled his head back so he could study her more closely. "Is this what the problem was all along?"

"For the most part. You have to understand, Zachary," she replied, her throat tight with emotion, "I completely reordered my life because of my . . . problem. My work, my career, those are my life, and I'm very happy this way. I've accepted it completely."

"So have I, Rachel. My career is the most important thing in my life—or was. Now you are."

"You're very important to me, too, Zachary. I'd never let my work get in the way of our relationship. It's just that marriage isn't an easy thing for me to think about. Marriage means family to me."

Zachary smoothed her hair with his hand in a comforting gesture. "Marriage doesn't mean *just* family, Rachel," he said softly. He knew there was more she was afraid of as well. "And it doesn't have to mean pain. All it takes is two people—the right people. And we are very right for each other." He tilted his head and kissed her, his lips warm on hers. "Besides, if we ever do want children, we could always adopt."

She tensed. "Wouldn't you want a child of your own? Your own flesh and blood?" She wanted so desperately to believe what he was saying, but part of her couldn't—perhaps never would.

Chuckling softly, Zachary eased the tension from her shoulders with his strong and knowing hands. "You make it sound as if I were out to select breeding stock."

"Zachary!"

"Well, you do! I want a lifetime partner, Rachel, not a broodmare."

His influence was calming. She felt her tensions start to disappear. He had said the words she'd longed for. "You are utterly outrageous, Zachary Lyons," she said, pushing playfully at his chest. "Give me one good reason why I should marry you."

His arms closed around her tightly, the intense light of seduction in his eyes. "If we hadn't exercised so much earlier, I'd give you more than one," he growled before his mouth closed over hers.

"Pace too much for you?" she murmured against his lips, a devilish light in her eyes.

"I'll show you pace!" he promised. But he was tender and gentle once he got her in his bedroom again.

The idea of marrying Zachary still frightened Rachel, but his hands seemed to wash away her fear as they caressed her. It was finally time to give her heart free rein again, she realized, time to admit to herself what her heart had known for quite a while: She was irretrievably in love with Zachary.

In the end, she supposed, it really didn't matter if the thought of loving him frightened her or if she had committed herself to what could be a painful path. The alternative would be much more painful. He had been right; she was much too involved to back out now. She still had her doubts about marriage, about Zachary's assurances concerning children, and particularly about what the passage of time might do to his convictions. But she didn't doubt her love. It was strong and real, and she would enjoy that love for as long as she could. Lying in his arms, feeling his hands caress and hold her till the aftershocks of their lovemaking quieted to a peaceful tremor, she was sure her love would last forever.

Zachary took her hand and slipped the ring on her finger. "There. That's better."

Rachel grinned. "Staking out your territory?"

"You'd better believe it, lady."

"Are you going to build another garage, to make a spot for me in your collection?" she said teasingly.

He took her hand and placed it on his chest. "I already have a spot for you right here, in my collection of one."

"Are you sure one will be enough?" she asked, her brow furrowed. "All I have to give you is myself."

"More than enough. All I want from you is yourself, for now and always. Children aren't important to me, Rachel."

"You're sure?"

Zachary sighed, the beginning of sleep showing in his eyes. "Very sure. As a matter of fact, I doubt I'd ever want to share you with anyone."

"Zachary?"

"Ssh," he murmured.

"Still thinking about it?"

"I'm thinking about sleeping," he mumbled, eyes closed.

They fell asleep, entwined in each other's arms.

Monday Rachel was back at work, catching up on the backlog from Friday and Saturday's business. She took a quick break halfway through the morning and wandered down to the shop, glad to see Martin with a backlog of his own.

"Good to see you so busy, Martin," she said, catching him with his body halfway under the hood of a very elderly Mercedes.

"Just a sec" came his muffled reply. He straightened up. "There," he said with a wink. "Nothing like German engineering and my ingenuity."

"Modest, too," she said, laughing.

"To a fault. Oh, by the way, congratulations."

"Congratulations? On what?"

"Zachary was here a while ago. He told me the good news."

"He what!"

Eyes full of amusement, Martin shook his head and chuckled. "Nobody supposed to know yet, right? That's our Zachary."

"Yes," she replied, fuming, "that's him all right."

"Well, anyway, I think it's great. About time someone snatched you up. And don't blame Zachary."

"Why not?" she asked.

"He was that way with the Duesenberg, too.

Could barely wait until I got it fixed before he wanted to take it out on the highway. Knowing Zachary, it can't be anytime at all before I'll be giving the bride away."

"Nothing's definite yet, Martin, but I'll keep you in mind."

Rachel made her way back to her office, where she found a note from Zachary. He had been called unexpectedly to Dallas and would be back tomorrow. Just like Zachary to be gone when she felt like a good fight!

The next afternoon, temper cooled, Rachel was back in her office when Angela buzzed her.

"Uh, Rachel?" Angela's voice came uncertainly over the intercom."

"Yes, Angela?"

"Your fiancé is here."

"My what!" Rachel cried.

"He made me say it."

"Zachary! Get in here!"

He opened the door as if expecting some object to come flying at his head. In point of fact, Rachel did have a paperweight in her hand. "Too pushy?" he asked.

"Definitely," Rachel replied, fighting a grin that eventually came through of its own accord. How could she stay mad at him?

"Then I suppose," he said as he came cautiously over to her desk, "I'd better not show you this." He held a folded newspaper in his hand.

She hefted the paperweight, and he placed the paper in front of her. She was wrong. She could stay mad at him. "Mr. Zachary Lyons and Ms. Rachel Jordan announce their engagement and impending marriage . . ." Rachel looked at him as if about to strangle him. "I may kill you," she stated quietly.

"Now, Rachel—"

"Two days ago you said you were going to give me time to think about it."

"You've had plenty of time to think. Besides, you are wearing the ring," he pointed out.

Rachel set down the paperweight and looked at her hand. The delicate ring of intertwined gold strands held a sparkling emerald. It surprised her how natural it felt on her finger and how quickly wearing a ring had become second nature to her again. "I am, I guess."

"Still mad?" he asked, coming around her desk.

"Yes."

"I should have consulted you, I suppose."

"Yes."

"Will you ever speak to me in more than one syllable again?" he asked.

She stared belligerently at him. "No, I won't."

"Aha!"

Rachel sighed and chuckled, then stood up and allowed herself to be pulled into his strong embrace. "What are you doing here? Other than annoying me, that is?"

Zachary kissed her deeply, leaving her gasping for air. "I knew you would appreciate my visit. But I can't stay long. I just stopped by to tell you the addition to your building just passed final inspection. You can begin moving things in now."

"Oh, good!" Rachel replied, pleasure showing on her face. "Do you know the first thing I'm moving over there?"

He released her and started to leave. "I have to be going now."

"It's bigger than a bread box," she said as he opened the door.

"Good-bye. See you later."

"That block of crushed metal! That's what! You remember that, don't you?" she called after him as he hurried out.

Rachel's laughter calmed down to a wide smile. She felt good. Her addition could open soon, her future seemed rosy, and—she was in love. She loved Zachary with all her heart and soul. In turn he had assured her that he wanted only her and that their full lives left little room for children anyway.

She looked down at the newspaper. It was only an announcement, nothing more. Here today, gone tomorrow. And it read, "impending marriage." Hardly anything concrete in that statement. But a wave of uneasiness passed over her, an uneasiness which had made itself felt often over the past few days. Sometimes it was severe enough to wake her in the morning sick to her stomach. It was probably just nerves. Lord knows she had enough on her mind. Yet, despite her uneasy feelings, a kind of calm acceptance had settled over her like a protective cloak. Like the calm before a storm.

CHAPTER NINE

Finally, thankfully, the big day arrived. The preparations and excitement of the grand opening took Rachel's mind off her uneasiness. Although very functional, the new addition was nevertheless a lovely structure of open spaces and hanging plants, decorated in an antique style. Rachel was immensely proud of the building and what it stood for: the success of her enterprise and her skill in running it.

She was also proud of the first-place trophy from the rally. The silver cup, engraved with her name and Zachary's and that of Jordan Motorcars, sat in regal, eye-catching honor on the hood of the brightly polished MG, which Zachary had brought in for display. He was proud, too, of the trophy, the building, and his car, but mainly he was proud of Rachel. His eyes barely left her all day.

Zachary loved to watch her. Her graceful movements, the fire in her eyes, the sound of her laughter excited him beyond measure. He wanted to marry her today, this instant, but he could bide his time. He knew she needed reassurance, and he was prepared to tell her anything she wanted to hear. As long as he could possess her totally, nothing else mattered. He would push, but he would push slowly.

Rachel thought it appropriate that Zachary should announce the winner of the contest. She did, however, feel a pang of jealousy when he delivered a quick kiss to the young lady who came closest to guessing the composition of the crushed metal block.

"Friend of yours?" Rachel asked coolly when she caught up to Zachary at the refreshment table.

"Are you accusing me of cheating?" he asked, his expression one of feigned shock.

"I'm accusing you of giving her the correct answer so you could congratulate her," Rachel replied. She accepted the glass of fruit punch he offered her.

He slipped his arm around her waist. "Never," he said innocently. "If I want to kiss someone, I just do it."

"Um-hm. Well, don't look now, Mr. Innocent, but there's lipstick on your cheek." She dabbed it off with a napkin, her eyes shining with amusement.

Zachary grabbed her hand and kissed her on the palm, his tongue secretly touching her sensitive skin. "The punch and cookies are good," he whispered, "but I'd rather have you." He reached over for one of the balloons floating nearby and handed her the string.

"Think this will buy my affections?" she asked.

"Just trying to keep both of your hands busy so I can ravish you without interference." They walked arm in arm, mingling with the crowd, Rachel's pink balloon bouncing behind her. "Is the opening a success?" Zachary asked.

"I'd say so. We've sold three cars, found two people who want to come in to interview for mechanic's positions, and," she replied, batting her eyelashes at him, "I've received several marriage proposals."

Zachary appeared unconcerned. "I've been telling everyone you're my fiancée, must have been someone I missed."

"Zachary!" She punched him lightly on the arm. "Besides, I said several."

"They'll have to wait in line."

"And if they're not that patient?" she said teasingly.

He shrugged. "They'll have to be. It will be several centuries at least before I'll give them a chance."

When all the punch, balloons, and people

were gone, Rachel sat in her new office, going over some credit applications. The bright, airy room still smelled pleasantly of sawdust and fresh paint. She had promoted Angela to assistant sales manager, giving the ecstatic young woman her old office, though Rachel had the big oak desk moved over to the new addition. It was now littered with receipts, bills, interview forms, and ledger sheets. Rachel slowly plodded through the paper work, wanting a clean desk before she went home.

Zachary knocked on her door and came in. "How about dinner?"

"Not tonight. I have to finish here, and today has left me sort of tired for some reason."

"Feeling okay?" he asked, looking concerned.

She smiled. "Fine. I think I'll just work here for a while, then go home to bed. Lunch tomorrow?"

"It's a date." He came over, kissed her, then turned to leave, stopping at the door. "You see how difficult things would be if we had children? Working late would be out of the question. Don't work too hard."

"I won't." She smiled at him as he left. He cared so deeply for her, yet he still allowed her the freedom her duties demanded. She was so glad he realized how much she needed that, and she knew he wouldn't change after they were married.

She brought herself up with a start. Even she was beginning to think of their marriage as

136

inevitable. She could not remember accepting the whole idea; it had simply become a part of her. The old fears were still there, too, but rapidly fading. When, she wondered, would he start talking about setting the date?

Her telephone rang, disrupting her reverie. "Rachel Jordan," she answered.

"Hi, honey, it's me."

"Oh, hi, Mom. You're early this month." Rachel and her mother, though never particularly close, still called each other once a month. Rachel usually talked about the business; her mother almost invariably kept her up-to-date on gossip concerning Bill's family.

Rachel's parents had had a very good marriage, and her mother simply couldn't understand how her daughter could be happy or fulfilled without a husband. She had been upset over Rachel's divorce and had taken a long time to accept it. Since then, she had never stopped telling her daughter to find a permanent man.

Rachel had been totally honest with her about the reason for the divorce, so now her mother also made sure to point out that there were many men who didn't want children. All she had to do was search and find the right man. *Well,* Rachel thought, *maybe I have.* But it was too early yet to tell her mother about Zachary, so she steeled herself for the usual conversation.

"Rachel, I have the most interesting news."

"Wait, don't tell me," Rachel said good-naturedly. "You found this incredible man who—"

"No, this is really interesting." Her mother continued, never breaking stride. "Bill and Claire are getting a divorce."

"Oh?" *That may be interesting to you, Mom,* she thought, *but not to me.*

"She filed on him. Mental cruelty, I think she said."

Now that was interesting. "Getting his progeny didn't improve his personality, I gather," Rachel replied sardonically.

"Evidently not. Claire and I had a talk the other day—we've become friends, you see—and she was quite distraught."

"I can imagine. Still, she does have more taste than I gave her credit for," Rachel said. Actually she was happy for Claire. It was good she had the sense and the nerve to walk out of a bad situation.

"But that's not the exciting part!"

Her mother's voice, usually calm and urbane, now fairly bubbled with excitement. It piqued Rachel's curiosity.

She leaned back in her chair, her paper work forgotten. "Well, are you going to tell me? Or do I have to guess?"

"You'd never guess. Not in a million years." There was a dramatic pause.

"Mother!"

"It seems, Rachel, that Bill was lying about his clean bill of health from that doctor. His sperm

138

count is so low that Claire had to be inseminated artificially in order to get pregnant—not once but several times and for both children. Poor Claire!"

Rachel sat, stunned, finally forcing herself to speak. "I don't understand."

"Don't you see, honey? Bill lied!"

That didn't surprise her at all. But her mind was still grasping for meaning. "Mother, it really makes no difference. I went to a doctor, too, remember?"

"Doctors! What do they know?" her mother said disdainfully. "Especially eight-odd years ago. Your tests weren't conclusive, were they?"

"Conclusive enough." Her mind was clamped shut on the subject, and she wished her mother wouldn't dredge all this up again.

"But there have been great strides in the study and treatment of fertility, Rachel. Besides, you never even got a second opinion, did you?"

"No." The mere thought of undergoing any more testing made Rachel cringe, then and now. Perhaps she was hiding from the truth, but she had good reason. "The doctor was very discouraging. Dismal, in fact." Though he had been vague about the results, he had flat-out told her she couldn't get pregnant. He wasn't very sympathetic either, she remembered. That was why, except for periodic checkups, she avoided doctors altogether, as well as any discussion of her problem.

"Still, all kinds of advances have taken place."

A plaintive note came to her mother's voice. "At my age some grandchildren would be very comforting."

"Mother, I'm thirty-five! And we've gone through all this before. I told you there's no chance of—"

"Now, Rachel, let's suppose a problem that couldn't be solved then is easily correctable now. Or suppose, just suppose"—her mother's voice became excited again—"in light of what I told you, that whatever problem you have was compounded by Bill's problem!"

"I don't—"

"If you had little chance of conceiving in the first place, what kind of chance would you have had with a man like Bill?"

Rachel's eyes widened in shock, her mother's words finally sinking in. "I—I—"

"With a lot of patience and a healthy, virile male . . ." She let her statement hang there.

Understanding suddenly hit Rachel like a shock wave. "Oh, God!"

"What's wrong, honey?"

"I've taken my problem for granted for years, lived with it. There are things, I—I mean, I never bothered with . . ." Zachary was a patient, healthy, virile male!

After a bad night that stretched into a bad morning, Rachel made her way to work. She felt slightly better after making an appointment with her doctor. She wasn't looking forward to it; she remembered very well the unpleasant tests of years ago. But her new doctor was a gentle and understanding woman who had calmed her down considerably, even over the phone.

When she hung up from talking to her mother the night before, she went straight home, barely remembering how she managed it. So when she arrived at her office, she expected to see her desk, still piled with the work she had left undone. She was met by a pleasant surprise.

"Angela! What are you doing?" Her new assistant sales manager had cleared her desk of work and was busy sorting her mail.

"Doing two jobs till your new secretary starts work next week. Remember?"

She hadn't. "Oh."

Angela smiled, but her eyes showed concern. "Rachel, is something wrong? It's not like you to leave so much work on your desk."

It wasn't like her to come to work this late either. She felt close to Angela and owed her an explanation. "I guess I have a lot on my mind," she said, sitting down behind her now-clean desk. "I have a doctor's appointment this afternoon."

Angela's brow furrowed. "Anything serious?"

"No," Rachel replied quickly. "No, I just have to check something. I'm fine. Really."

"Good." She looked relieved. "I'll be in the other building if you need me."

The day seemed to drag by until her twelve

thirty appointment. Rachel found herself almost delighted by the prospect. Her appointment today was only the beginning of what she knew could be a long road, but one which could end in determining the need for and a method of contraception. Never in her wildest dreams had she thought such measures necessary, not after the day her former doctor, in his brash and unfeeling manner, had assured her she was sterile. She cautioned herself to remember he might have been right.

Rachel felt more than a little chagrined as she carefully filled her doctor in on her history—something she should have done a long time ago. But the problem had never come up in her regular checkups, and, she admitted, she had been scared. That fear had caused her to behave like a foolish teen-ager. Thank goodness the truth had come out in time!

The doctor, however, was very understanding and sounded pleased Rachel had finally decided to delve into the matter again. Her patient's history now complete, she was cautious but encouraging.

Rachel's initial exam, though much longer and mysteriously more involved than usual, was over fairly quickly, and afterward Dr. Helen Morgan asked to see her in her office. She was glancing over some papers when Rachel walked in.

"Have a seat, Rachel."

"Thank you."

"That wasn't too bad, was it?"

"Not at all." She could barely contain herself. "Well?"

Helen Morgan chuckled and laid aside the papers she was reading. "It's not that simple, Rachel." She took off her glasses and put them in her pocket. Her blue eyes sparkled as she looked at her patient. "I may want you to check in with a specialist sometime, so we can do more detailed testing."

"Specialist!" Rachel cried, alarmed.

Dr. Morgan held up her hand. "Take it easy! Nothing serious at all, I assure you. There are just a few things that should be, um, looked into," she said with a laugh. "If you'll excuse the expression."

Rachel gripped the arms of her chair. "They won't have to do that carbon dioxide test again, will they?" The painful memory of years ago jumped to mind.

"The Rubin test? No, that won't be necessary."

"But you suspect something?" Rachel asked quietly.

Again the doctor laughed. "Twenty years' practicing my poker face with patients, and I still haven't got it right. Yes, I suspect something."

"What?"

She shook her head. "I'll know more tomorrow, and I'll call and tell you once the preliminary test results are back. Blood work,

143

urinalysis, that sort of thing. Then we'll see how we want to proceed."

"You're not going to tell me anything?" Rachel asked in a strained voice.

Dr. Morgan got up and came around her desk, then patted Rachel's hand as she ushered her out the door. "You're healthy, fit, and trim, Rachel. There's nothing to worry about. I'll call tomorrow."

It was nearly three when Rachel got back to her office, and she found a very angry Zachary waiting for her.

"Hi. Remember me?" he asked, a touch of sarcasm in his voice.

Rachel clapped her hand to her mouth. She'd forgotten their lunch date! "I'm sorry, Zachary. I—I had to go out for a while. I completely forgot about lunch."

"Evidently. I called, and they said you weren't in. I came over, and even Angela didn't know where you were."

Angela, bless her! Rachel didn't want Zachary to know how foolish she'd been. "I had a doctor's appointment I forgot about. But I'm starving. Still want lunch?" she asked, blustering through before he could ask questions.

Zachary clearly wasn't too angry. He simply smiled and said, "Yes. I still want lunch."

It was pleasant going to lunch late; the service was fast and the crowds were almost nonexistent. Rachel was surprised to find her appetite had returned. It seemed being told by a doctor

144

you were healthy, fit, and trim made you hungry.

After lunch Rachel ran into an unexpected problem. "You've already taken most of the day off. Why not come home for a workout?" Zachary asked, his eyebrows raised rakishly.

"Oh!" She chuckled nervously. "Sounds nice, but as you said, I've been gone most of the day as it is. I really need to get back to work." They were standing in a fairly secluded part of the Jordan Motorcars parking lot. Suddenly she felt very vulnerable.

He shrugged his acceptance. "See you tonight then?"

Rachel looked startled. This wasn't going to be easy. "Um, I'm afraid I've got another late night ahead of me."

Now Zachary looked suspicious. "What is this? Another cooling-off period?" he asked, irritation in his voice.

"No, really, I—"

"Rachel," Zachary said, pulling her close to him as they stood by his car in the parking lot, "what's going on? I hope you're not still worried I might change my mind about children. There aren't many more ways I can think of to convince you." She could see his patience was wearing thin.

"It's not that." She did believe him. And she was in the process of making sure they didn't have any surprises in store for them. "I just have to work late and—"

145

"Bull!" He pressed his hard, lean form intimately against hers, making her feel his desire. "If I don't get you alone soon, I'm going right out of my mind," he said, his voice a whispered growl.

Rachel's own desire for Zachary was mounting, too, and she couldn't deny it or him. "I'll explain tomorrow night." Until she knew how vulnerable she might be, she had to keep away from him until she could take some precautions. One thing was sure: She was all too vulnerable to his charms. A moment longer in his arms, and she would find herself agreeing, going home with him. One time, just once . . . stop it! One more time just might be *the* time. "See you tomorrow night!" she said, her voice filled with promise. Breaking free of his grasp, she nearly ran into the showroom.

Zachary, puzzled and irritated, watched her depart, then got into his car and took off. He had promised her time, but it was getting damned hard to let her have it. Tomorrow night he would have to press her to set the date.

Rachel passed another restless night, then fidgeted and jumped every time the phone rang the next day. Luckily Angela was too busy to notice her discomfort, or she might have pressed for an explanation.

When at last the call did come, it only made her worry more: Dr. Morgan wanted to talk to Rachel in person. She took a cab, feeling too nervous to drive, and along the way cursed her-

146

self for allowing the small ray of hope back into her life. She had been perfectly happy, accepting the knowledge she would never conceive children. She had been satisfied with her life as it was. Now she was back in turmoil. She would not have done this for anyone but Zachary, not even herself.

The wait to see Dr. Morgan was short, but for Rachel it seemed like a lifetime. "Okay. Tell me the bad news," she blurted out as soon as she entered the doctor's office.

Dr. Morgan unfolded her glasses and put them on to peer over the top of the lenses at Rachel. "If you sit any closer to the edge of your seat, you'll fall off." She watched with approval as Rachel settled back in the chair in front of her desk. "Now then, what I have to tell you is not usually considered bad news. As a matter of fact, I often inform my patients of their test results over the phone. She referred to the sheaf of papers in her hands. "Yours, however, is a special case."

"But the other doctor—"

"I won't discuss the findings of your former physician," Dr. Morgan said, her voice holding a sharp, professional edge. "That's between you, him, and possibly your lawyer. In all fairness, however, I will say that the advances in fertility research even in the last two years—let alone ten—are incredibly complex and hard to keep up with."

"I don't understand."

"How much do you know about your condition?"

"My former physician was very discouraging. He said my test results were dismal."

Helen smiled. "It's amazing how advances in medicine can turn accepted ideas into myths and how reluctant some people are to accept the truth. I imagine you weren't told much about the actual mechanics of the problem."

"Nothing at all really," Rachel admitted.

"Another thing that amazes me is the different attitudes toward revealing test results." She shook her head. "You have a tipped uterus, Rachel. At one time I considered discussing the matter with you, but you always seemed in a hurry and uninterested. I gathered you weren't sexually active. I was busy, too, so it never seemed that important. Also, the condition isn't considered that big a problem now."

"But he told me I was sterile."

Again Dr. Morgan turned all professional. "I can't tell you why that is. As I said, that's between you and him." Her voice softened. "To be told all you were told, in addition to the discomfort you experienced in your infertility work-up —well, I can certainly understand your decision to drop the matter entirely."

Rachel shifted in her chair at the doctor's accurate description of her feelings. "So what do you have to tell me?"

"A tipped uterus is now known not to be a cause of infertility in and of itself. The fact that many such cases were caused by scarring or pelvic adhesions probably led to those early conclusions. If the condition is congenital—as your X rays indicate—it can make it more difficult to get pregnant but certainly not impossible. However, as in your case at the time, if your mate has a reduced sperm count, the odds are significantly reduced."

So her mother was right! Her problem had been compounded by Bill's. "I'm not sterile?"

Dr. Morgan looked startled, then leaned back and laughed heartily. "No. Definitely not."

"But I do have a problem?"

Her laughter settled to a warm smile. "You may have, I don't know. There may be things to be concerned about, some of which might require a specialist, most of which will require more tests than I can conduct capably. I can, however, do quite nicely with what I called you in to tell you."

Rachel's hands clenched the arms of her chair until her knuckles turned white. "And that is?"

"Whatever fertility problems you have are academic now, Rachel. You're pregnant! Just about three weeks as a matter of fact."

For the first time in her life, Rachel came close to fainting. She felt as if all the blood were draining from her head. "Would—would you repeat that, please?" she managed to stammer after a few minutes.

Dr. Morgan took off her glasses and went to

149

Rachel's side. "Your face went quite pale. Do you need to lie down?"

"No—no, I'm fine. Did you really say I'm pregnant?"

"Quite definitely. I had my suspicions the other day, but I wanted to see your test results." She looked concerned. "That's why I wanted you here. I thought this was probably going to be a shock. I take it you had no suspicions of your own?"

"I thought I couldn't—I mean, I never—"

"Took precautions?" the doctor offered.

Rachel nodded.

Dr. Morgan's face turned serious. "Do you want the child?" she asked sympathetically.

Her head spinning, Rachel gave the best answer she could. "I—I don't know."

"Will the father?"

Zachary. Since his proposal he had assured her he didn't want children. He had repeated those assurances so often and so convincingly that she had come to believe them without doubt. She shook her head despairingly. "I don't know."

Helen Morgan's voice was sympathetic, her manner calm and reassuring. "Then you have much to think about and decide. Whenever you need someone to talk to, you know I'm here. I must tell you that with your condition, special attention may be required. But there is absolutely no reason why you can't bring a healthy, happy baby into this world." In a tender gesture that brought tears to Rachel's eyes, Dr. Morgan kissed her lightly on the cheek. "Now I'm afraid I have another patient. A young woman in her last trimester! I suppose I'll be called to the hospital at three in the morning again." She sighed happily and hurried out the door.

CHAPTER TEN

Her whole world had turned upside down. Rachel had been afraid of losing Zachary because she couldn't have children. Finally, though, Zachary's affection and constant assurances had made her realize that was a false fear. But now she was pregnant, and Zachary's attitudes and reassurances, once convincing and comforting, now seemed ominous. No regrets for not having children could mean deep regrets for getting trapped with a woman who was pregnant. He had, after all, taken great pains to tell her he didn't want children, that he wanted her and only her to share his life.

Aside from those dismal thoughts, she had her own ambiguous feelings to contend with. Helen Morgan's question returned to her again and again. Did she want the child? Deep inside,

Rachel knew the answer was a most definite yes. She was carrying a human life inside her, a miracle, made even more miraculous by her medical and personal history. Yet she realized that years of dedication to her career and Jordan Motorcars had indeed made her somewhat selfish and jealous of her time. Could she change? Did she want to? One thing was sure: One way or another, she was in for the biggest period of adjustment in her life, and she might very well end up in it alone.

She left the doctor's office in a daze, glad she hadn't taken her own car. She went home, called Angela to tell her she wouldn't be back that day because she needed to run some errands, then stretched out on her bed. She hated to lie, but she didn't feel up to explanations just yet.

She felt very tired. Was it the pregnancy or just the stress of the past two days? Trying unsuccessfully to fall asleep, Rachel lay there in semidarkness and gave herself up to her thoughts.

Zachary would accept responsibility for the child, she knew that without question. He might be impetuous and eccentric, but he was not one to shirk responsibility. They had a date this evening; she could tell him then, but did she want to? Did she want him shouldering a burden he had gone to such lengths to assure her he didn't want?

All the times he told her he didn't want chil-

153

dren, all the stress he put on her career and an unencumbered life-style, all his once-comforting words came back to her with new significance. Yes, he would accept his responsibility as the father of the new life inside her, but he wouldn't be happy about it. It would be a burden, a restriction, a fact of life he would live with and resent her for. Unless he didn't know. Unless she didn't tell him.

The walls of her bedroom seemed to close in around her, so she got up and went to the kitchen to make some coffee. She thought of the list of dos and don'ts the doctor had given her, decided against the caffeine, and settled for a glass of milk. *Odd,* she thought, *I don't even like milk that much.* But she drank it anyway. The calcium was good for the baby. Maybe Dr. Morgan could suggest a substitute. . . .

And then it hit her. She would drink milk, take vitamins, whatever else was required. She wanted the baby, wanted to bring it to full term. After it was born, adoption was a possibility—if she was able to give her baby up. After all, boy or girl, it would be the only thing left of what she and Zachary had shared.

She couldn't tell him, wouldn't tell him. A marriage of regret was what she had feared before and was certain of now. If she explained everything, she would be trapping him, and that would eventually drive a wedge between them. When she and Bill had divorced, there were no children to consider, so the break was clean. But

154

Zachary was not Bill. Rachel loved him too much to put him in the position of being trapped into a marriage he didn't want.

She would have the baby to comfort her after Zachary was gone. The pain wouldn't last forever, and Zachary would have his freedom.

"You look especially lovely this evening," Zachary told her when he picked her up at eight.

"Thank you." Rachel felt her throat tighten involuntarily at the sight of him. "You look especially handsome." He had on his camel-colored suit, his shirt unbuttoned at the neck showing his tanned skin. He nearly took her breath away.

She wore a low-cut knit dress of oyster white which hugged her figure. Soon enough, with her slim build, such fashions would be impossible to wear. His eyes lingered on her appreciatively, reluctant to let her out of his sight. "I stopped by your office earlier. Angela said you were out running errands."

"Just some shopping. A reward for working so hard." She didn't have to tell him tonight that she wanted to break off the engagement. There would be plenty of time. But a voice inside her told her the longer she waited, the harder the task would be. "I have something to tell you."

Before she could go any further, however, Zachary pulled her into his arms and kissed her, his tongue chasing her passionately in the warm cavern of her mouth. He held her tightly, not wanting to let her go. She was so beautiful he was afraid she might disappear before his eyes. "You certainly do. You have to explain why you've been neglecting me. See how selfish I am? I could never share you."

"Oh, Zachary," she said, hugging him tightly, her eyes squeezed shut. How she loved him! But his words only assured her she was right.

"But let's get the dinner part of this evening over with first. There will be plenty of time for talking later. Among other things," he added with raised eyebrows.

Yes. One last evening. She forced herself to smile, and it wasn't hard. She always felt like smiling when she looked at him. "You wouldn't be thinking of taking advantage of me, now would you?"

"Now, later, and every chance I get," he replied with a sly grin. He was glad she was back to her old self again. She had appeared so strained earlier. He hurried her off to dinner.

Rachel tried to forget what she must do later and simply enjoyed being with him. They had a wonderful meal in an intimate, outrageously expensive restaurant. Rachel felt very glad she hadn't forgone this particular date. Zachary must have made reservations days in advance.

Afterward they went dancing. Their dancing always seemed to Rachel to be a prelude to making love. Zachary's graceful, powerful movements and his gentle, exciting hands created a delicious tension throughout her body. She abandoned herself completely to his touch and the intense, alive sensations he aroused in her.

The entire evening seemed designed to arouse them both. For Zachary it was an important night in their relationship, even more important than the night he had proposed. Then everything had been vague, a trial. Tonight he wouldn't leave her until a date for their marriage was set. To him Rachel was more than a woman; she was temptation itself. And he could no longer continue in the uncertain world of trials.

They left the dance floor and went to Rachel's because it was close by, because they could barely stand to break contact with each other for even a moment, and because Rachel wanted this last night they made love to be in her bed. She hoped the memories would be stronger, warmer there, able to comfort her on lonely nights to come.

The ride home was quiet. They were filled with their own thoughts of the sweet lovemaking to come.

"Love me, Zachary," Rachel pleaded as they slowly undressed each other, drawing out the pleasurable torment. Zachary's face softened with the love he held for Rachel. She heard his sharp intake of breath as the last of her clothing was removed and she stood before him. Her heart leaped as he folded her into his arms, the comfort and warmth drawing her closer to where she truly belonged.

157

Rachel nuzzled against his welcoming body with a sigh, savoring the feeling of his bare flesh against hers. Inhaling the heady fragrance of his masculine skin, she felt her desire shooting to the surface and began to set the pace for their gentle loving.

Zachary sensed her mood and followed her lead, lowering them to the bed. His sensitive tongue traced the delicate contours of her face, darting down to her quivering, parted lips, running along strong white teeth and gently nibbling on her soft lower lip before taking total control of her mouth. Her tongue thrust out to meet his, as Rachel moaned softly, seductively, her hands clutching his shoulders. His lips closed over one exquisitely sensitive nipple, sucking gently, his tongue coaxing her rosy softness into a hard button. Then he moved on to allow her other throbbing breast the same delicious pleasures. Rachel shivered with joy as he began anew, his fingers stroking her femininity with a feathery touch.

Her hands began an exploration of their own. Rachel wanted to roam over every inch of his body, savoring, touching, memorizing what lay beneath her eager lips and fingertips. She lovingly traced his face, her eyes closed, pressing the shape of his finely chiseled features into memory.

She could never forget those dark eyes, fringed with black, lush lashes, or the changing expressions they were capable of. Her fingers moved down to his neck and shoulders, such strong, muscled shoulders narrowing down his broad chest to a trim waist. She traced the contours of his stomach and firm buttocks before continuing on to enjoy his hard, powerful thighs, those sexy calves and well-formed feet. She started there, letting her lips and tongue commit to memory every inch of his body until he couldn't take any more.

"Rachel, please," he murmured huskily as she ran her tongue across the smooth ridges of his belly. "Oh—" He gasped. Whatever he was going to say was lost as Rachel dipped lower and continued to explore every part of him. "I'm going to explode any minute, sweet Rachel, if you don't stop that now." He groaned as her lips, body, and hands covered him. He was losing control.

Abruptly Zachary pulled her on top of him as he thrust his tongue into the hot and willing cavern of her mouth. He savored the feel of her surrounding him before starting the gentle rhythm that would bring them to the dizzying heights of ecstasy.

"Now comes your loving, sweet Rachel," he whispered as she trembled against him, ready for the sweet release he held from her. His hands roamed over her until she cried out in joy, her body joining with his as they climbed the mountain together, only to fall back to earth, wrapped in each other's arms.

When rational thought returned, Rachel's

mind immediately wandered to the new life she carried. She had been assured by her doctor that making love wouldn't harm her child. She needed Zachary this one last time, needed a memory to carry with her as their child grew inside her.

Rachel's body had yet to start any of the normal changes brought on by pregnancy. Her slimness denied the life growing within. Yet she knew it was there, felt the life growing strongly in her womb.

Zachary wondered at Rachel's serene calmness. She was so relaxed, so tranquil. The anxiety and nervousness of the last few days seemed to have vanished. The tensions they had both felt recently seemed to have disappeared before his very eyes. He didn't know the reason why, but he was relieved to see her so relaxed. Maybe, he hoped, she had finally come to accept that they were destined to be married.

"It's time to set a date, Rachel," Zachary whispered in her ear. "I can't wait any longer for you to be my wife."

Rachel swung her feet to the floor and wrapped her robe around her. The feeling of calm lingered. She knew what she had to do and say. It would be difficult, but she would do it—for herself, for the baby, for Zachary. She would do it because she loved him and because the pain of parting now would be nothing compared to the pain of losing his love in a slowly declining marriage of regret. "I can't be your wife, Zachary. Not now or ever."

Zachary had watched her movements languidly, but when she spoke, he sat bolt upright. "What?"

She turned to face him, steeling her nerves and making her voice sound as casual as possible. "I can't be your wife or anyone's. Marriage isn't for me."

He got up, his face registering only disbelief. "You've decided that, have you?" The barest edge of anger sounded in his voice.

"Yes."

"You decided you don't want to be married, just like that, all by yourself?"

"Don't patronize me!" Her pain was becoming anger, and she let it. Anger was much easier to deal with.

Zachary came over to her and grabbed her by the shoulders. "Don't be insane, Rachel. You know what we've found is special. We're perfect for each other."

Not quite perfect, she thought sorrowfully. He didn't want children, and she was pregnant. She tried to turn away from him. "You can't force me, dammit! I've made up my mind."

He shook her slightly. "Then you can damn well unmake it! I'm not letting you go!"

Finally she succeeded in breaking free of his grasp and retreated a few steps away. "You'll have to. The engagement is off. And it's best if we don't see each other again." She left him standing in the bedroom, a look of pain and anger in his eyes.

It was a few moments before he followed her to the living room, and when he did, he was dressed and obviously ready for battle. His eyes blazed with an intense inner light. "None of this makes any sense, Rachel. I'm not doing anything without an explanation. Right now!"

"I've given you all the answers I have to give. I don't want to marry you," she replied, feeling as if she were about to fall apart.

Zachary ran his hand over his face, obviously trying to control his temper. "And you don't want to see me anymore, right?" he said through clenched teeth.

"I don't see any point in it. You'd only keep badgering me to get married and make me miserable."

"Damn right I would!"

"See?"

"I don't see anything at all!" he yelled. Gradually, visibly, he calmed himself. "Would you kindly give me an explanation?"

"There's nothing to explain, I told you that. You want to get married; I don't. You wouldn't let up on me; I won't stand for that. I've been looking for an easy way to tell you all this, but I couldn't find one. So I'm telling you now."

"And what we just shared?" he asked vehemently, jabbing his finger toward the bedroom. "What we've shared all along?"

Rachel didn't know how much longer she

could keep up this charade. Her heart was already aching. "Face it, Zachary. It's over. It's been wonderful, but it's over."

Zachary slowly shook his head from side to side, as if clearing his mind of her last statement. "No." He turned around for a moment, then turned back, accusation in his black eyes. "It's still the same problem, isn't it? You still think I'll regret marrying you because you can't have children."

"Zachary—"

"So you're doing this out of some crazy belief that you're saving me from myself."

In a way he was right, but he had the reasoning backward. She wasn't going to trap him with a child he didn't want. "Zachary, accept it. I don't want to see you anymore. Children have nothing to do with it."

"Bull!" He walked over and sat beside her on the couch. "What else can I say? I don't want children Rachel, I want you—only you. I'll say it a million times if you want me to. I'll engrave it in gold. I'm too selfish to be a father." Zachary was pulling things out of the air now, saying whatever he could, whatever he thought she wanted to hear. He needed her, wanted her, and knew she felt the same way.

Tears started forming in Rachel's eyes. With every word he cut her a little more, tore at her heart a little harder. "Stop it! Stop it!"

He had to get through to her somehow. Even if he had to make things up about himself, he would. "I'll never change my mind, Rachel, never. I hate children. Can't stand them. Always underfoot and in the way. I—"

With a heart-rending sob Rachel tore herself away from him and threw herself toward the front door, her vision obscured by tears. She couldn't stand it anymore. She had been right, so right. "I hate you!" she cried, opening the door with a jerk. "Get out!"

"Rachel, please!"

"Get out!" she screamed, breaking down and sobbing hysterically.

Zachary stood, his heart going out to her. "Sweet Rachel—" Then he saw the look in her eyes, and his blood chilled. "All right. I'm going." As he stood at the door, he reached out and gently brushed the tears from her face. She pulled away. "Good-bye, Rachel."

And Zachary Lyons walked through the door and out of her life.

CHAPTER ELEVEN

Rachel blinked back tears as she made sure the door was locked and the security chain on. Then she sank to her knees and wept bitterly. Each deep, ragged breath only started the tears anew.

Fifteen minutes passed with only the sound of her sobs, and then came a knock on the door.

"Go away," she mumbled to herself.

Again the knock and then the doorbell. Whoever it was was certainly persistent. At last she got shakily to her feet, wiped her eyes and blew her nose, and opened the door as far as the chain would allow. "Yes?"

"Let me in."

Her heart jumped. "Zachary, just go away."

"No way. Let me in or stand back," he said threateningly.

"This won't do any good. We've said all we've

got to say to each other. Just go away and leave me alone."

Zachary placed one hand on the door and pushed. One quick, hard movement and the chain pulled out of the door. He walked in and closed the door behind him. "Remind me to show you how to install one of those properly."

Rachel retreated into the living room. "Wha-what do you want?" His eyes were more intense than she had ever seen them, though he appeared calm. "I thought you—"

"Left?" He interrupted with a laugh. "Haven't you learned yet, Rachel? I'm not that easy to get rid of. You're lucky I did leave for a while. Otherwise I would have turned you over my knee and paddled that lovely rear of yours."

"Then what do you want?"

"Answers. All of them."

She looked away. "I've told you all there is. There's nothing more to say."

"The hell there isn't! You love me!" he said, reaching out a hand and turning her back to face him.

"Such modesty," she returned sarcastically.

"I know you love me because I'm so familiar with the symptoms. I love you, too."

Why did he have to torment her? *Of course I love you*, she wanted to scream; *that's why I'm doing this*. "Why don't you just leave?"

"Didn't you hear what I said? I love you, Rachel, but I'm through listening to your lies."

Tears started rolling down her face again. "I-I'm not lying, I—"

"Stop it! No more!" He sat down on the couch, pulling her with him. She tried to get up, but he stopped her. "Sit down and start talking, Rachel. I'll not stand for any more of this foolish behavior."

Rachel pulled her hands free of his grasp and beat them on his chest, with little effect. "Push, push, push," she cried, her words barely recognizable through her tears. "That's all you know how to do. Push!" She buried her face in her hands and sobbed. "I can't take it anymore."

Zachary looked at her sympathetically, waiting for her to get the tears out of her system. She was tired and angry, he could see that, and it hurt him to browbeat her like this. But he was tired, too, tired of waiting, and he wouldn't leave without an answer from her. "Then tell me the truth," he commanded softly.

Her crying slowed to a standstill. She felt as if she had no more tears in her. She dried her eyes and looked at him, seeing a mixture of anger, concern, and tenderness in his expression. He wouldn't leave her alone; she saw that, too. He loved her, and he would never leave her alone until he knew. "Maybe you do have a right to know. But," she warned him seriously, "it won't make any difference. I won't accept any noble gestures, Zachary. I won't!"

"Noble gestures?" A feeling of utter confusion came over him. He slumped against the back of

167

the couch and sighed. "Perhaps you'd better start from the beginning, Rachel. I don't have the slightest idea what you're talking about."

She felt her composure returning. He did have a right to know. The child was his, too. She should never have tried to hide it from him, but she realized she had done so because she was afraid: afraid of telling him, afraid of standing up to him. It was fear which had gotten her into this mess in the first place. If she hadn't been too afraid to find out what was really wrong with her, she wouldn't have to give up Zachary now. It was time to stop being afraid.

She would make it clear to him she didn't expect him to shoulder any responsibility, and then, finally, he would leave her alone. "This is entirely my responsibility, Zachary," she said firmly. "I've done a foolish thing, and the responsibility is all mine. Do you understand?"

He nodded, though he didn't understand anything at all.

"My fertility problem—"

Zachary started to say something, saw the look she gave him, and thought better of it. He leaned back on the couch.

"My fertility problem turned out not to be a problem at all. I have a slightly different internal structure from most women, and that difference, combined with a husband who was not as fertile as he said he was, caused us to remain childless." Zachary leaned forward, a frown of concentration on his face as he absorbed what she was saying. "I then believed an incompetent doctor, who assured me I was sterile. I'm not."

Zachary's eyebrows arched in surprise, his face brightening. "But, Rachel, that's wonderful! You were simply misled. That's not foolish."

"No, but it was foolish not to get another opinion. Foolish not to pursue the matter because I was afraid. And very foolish to assume I was sterile simply because someone told me I was."

"But there's no harm done. I don't understand why—"

"Sterile women don't need to bother with precautions when they make love." She looked at him sharply, gauging his reaction. "I'm pregnant, Zachary. Three weeks pregnant, to be exact."

The look of shock on his face was total. "With . . ." he started to say, having to clear his throat before he could continue, "With my child?"

His reaction would have made her laugh under other circumstances. But she knew why he looked so startled. "I had hoped to spare you the trouble of figuring out a way to extricate yourself from the relationship."

Zachary, barely listening to her, stood up and walked across the room, his back to her. He held up his hand in a plea for silence.

"Knowing how you feel about children—"

"Will you be quiet for a moment?" he ordered in a near whisper. "I've just been told I'm going to be a father."

"But don't you see? That's what I'm telling

you, Zachary. It's my responsibility, my mistake. I won't trap you into this. You thought you were marrying a woman who couldn't get pregnant."

"Will you be quiet!" he demanded, turning to face her, a look of quiet wonder in his eyes. "All that nonsense about not wanting to get married, not wanting to see me again. It was all an act, wasn't it?"

Rachel nodded. "Though I did hate you for a moment. It wasn't pleasant to hear your views on children again, not now that I'm carrying a child."

"Our child," he said in correction. He came over and sat down beside her. "Our child," he repeated slowly.

She had thought he understood. "Yes, a demanding, time-wasting, always-underfoot child," she said, throwing his own words back at him to make him face facts.

He smiled smugly. "What's the matter? You think you're the only one who can act?"

"What?" she asked, frowning.

"I would have told you anything, Rachel, done anything. I thought you were still worried about my backing out. I said what I thought you wanted to hear, assured you I hated children because I thought you were worried I'd want some one day and leave you the way Bill did." He slapped his forehead in chagrin. "Oh, God, did I almost wreck everything."

It was Rachel's turn to be totally confused. "What are you saying?"

He hugged her, then let her go to look deeply into her eyes. "Let's promise not to lie to each other anymore, ever. We nearly destroyed the best thing that ever happened to us."

It was clear to her he was a good actor, but was he acting then or now? "I told you, Zachary. I won't accept any noble gestures on your part."

Zachary tipped his head back and laughed. "Rachel, you really don't understand, do you?" he said, not waiting for an answer. He pulled her close and kissed her soundly. "I love you—all of you." He patted her stomach tenderly. "I think I fell in love the moment we met."

"But you thought I couldn't—"

Zachary put his finger to her lips. "It didn't take long before I knew I wanted to make you mine forever, whether we ended up with no children or a dozen. Don't you see?" he asked, seeing the doubtful expression on her face. "I knew all that before you said a word about your problem or your past, and learning it didn't change the way I feel. Neither will this or anything that may happen in the future."

"You—you want the child?"

"What I said when you first told me about your supposed problem is still true. I hadn't thought much about children one way or another. But I wanted you very much. Now that we have a child on the way, I want it very much, too. Don't you?" he asked.

"Yes, but some of the things you said, about

our lives already being so full, they make so much sense."

"We are quite set in our ways and like it that way, but maybe that's not such a good thing. There's more to life than work. I think we both will do quite a bit of growing right along with the baby. I, for one, am looking forward to it."

Tears brimmed in her eyes, but this time they were tears of joy. She wrapped her arms around his neck, hugging him fiercely. "I love you, Zachary. I love you so much." She covered his face with tender kisses, and he returned each one.

"I think it's way past time we set a date, sweet Rachel."

"I—oh, Zachary . . ." she began hesitantly. Everything was moving so fast she felt dizzy. All that had happened in the past few days left her unsure of herself, unwilling to take anything at face value. She loved him, and he loved her; that was all she wanted to think about. "Now that we have each other, we have all the time in the world."

Zachary recognized the uncertainty in her eyes but didn't let her know he saw the doubt lingering there. "We don't have to decide anything right now, honey. It's been quite a night for both of us. What you need most is sleep, and that's exactly what you're going to get." He smiled to himself when he saw the relief his statement brought to her face.

"Yes," she said, realizing for the first time how

very tired she was. She felt physically and emotionally exhausted. "I could sleep for a week."

"Come on now, I'm going to put you to bed. Do you think some warm milk might help?" he inquired solicitously as he led her to the bedroom.

Warm milk? Yech! She could tolerate milk ice cold, but warm? No way. "Zachary, all I need is for you to hold me in your arms," she assured him.

He helped tuck her into bed, then joined her, pulling her willing body into his arms. She was soon breathing deeply. Sleep didn't come so quickly to Zachary, however. He had much to do tomorrow, and planning filled his thoughts until he, too, dozed off.

Zachary awoke to find Rachel wrapped around his warm body. He drank in the sight of her sleeping so peacefully, the serenity of her face bringing peace to him also. She mumbled something, turning away from him and stretching before curling into sleep again.

He carefully separated himself from her and quietly dressed before leaving the bedroom. He needed to get organized and start his plans in motion.

Calling Jordan Motorcars first, he told Angela that Rachel wouldn't be in that day and asked to speak to Martin.

"Hey, Zach, what's up?" Martin asked without bothering with pleasantries.

"Rachel and I are getting married this Satur-

173

day. Still want to give the bride away?" he inquired, already knowing the answer.

"Who's bringing the shotgun?" he asked, laughing. "Seriously, name the time and place, and I'll be there, tuxedo and all," Martin added, the joy and excitement clearly evident in his voice.

"Bring the shotgun just in case, and I'll have to get back to you on the specifics." Zachary checked his watch and continued crisply. "In the meantime, would you inform the staff and tell them they're all invited, but not a word of all this to Rachel, okay?"

"Be glad to," Martin said. "Zach, is Rachel all right?"

"Yes, just tired. I'll explain everything when I see you," Zachary told him before hanging up. Martin could and would handle any problems that came up at the shop. That was one less worry.

Whom to call next, his mother, Rachel's mother, or her doctor? He juggled the different time zones for a moment. Her doctor. It helped in situations like this that Rachel was such an organized person. Her address book held everything he needed.

"Dr. Helen Morgan, please."

"Who shall I say is calling?"

"Zachary Lyons. This concerns Rachel Jordan."

"Hold, please."

Zachary paced impatiently, waiting forever,

it seemed, until the doctor came on the line. "Dr. Morgan here."

"This is Zachary Lyons. I'd like to make an appointment with you."

"Um, I'm an ob-gyn, Mr. Lyons."

"Yes, I know. I'd like to discuss Rachel Jordan's condition. I'm the child's father," he informed her.

"Oh! Certainly. Can you make it this afternoon?" she inquired calmly.

"Yes."

"And, Zachary, feel free to bring Rachel in with you," she said after telling him what time.

After making airline reservations, he called his mother.

"Zachary, is something wrong?" she asked immediately.

He chuckled at her worried tone, realizing that he never called her during the day. "Only if you think my getting married is wrong, Mother," he told her, still laughing.

"Married! Oh, Zachary, who . . . when . . . oh, my . . ." She trailed off in surprise.

Zachary quickly explained and informed her of his plans, told her of the airline tickets waiting for her and assured her that she would have time to shop for a dress after arriving in Houston. He would pick her up at the airport that evening.

Walking quietly into the bedroom, he assured himself that Rachel was still sleeping before calling her mother. "Mrs. Jordan, this is Zachary

Lyons. I'm a friend of your daughter, Rachel. As a matter of fact, I'm going to marry her."

Her reaction was nearly the same as his mother's had been. He filled her in on all the details, assured her that he would pick her up at the airport and that she would have time to buy a dress for the wedding. She could go shopping with his mother. He also requested she not call Rachel just yet.

After arranging for the church, marriage license, and blood test, he went again to check on Rachel. He had just stepped into the bedroom when he heard her small alarm clock click in preparation to going off. He leaped across the room, tried unsuccessfully to turn it off, and was just stuffing it into his pocket when it went off.

Rachel's emerald eyes fluttered open. She looked at him, at the buzzing bulge in his pocket, and at the startled look on his face. "Kinky, Zachary. Very kinky."

"I just didn't want it to wake you," he said.

"Um-hmm. You sure you two don't want to be alone?" she asked in a teasing voice.

"Just help me turn this thing off. It tickles."

Rachel reached into his pocket and fumbled for a moment, finally succeeding in quieting the alarm. "There." Zachary started to get undressed. "What are you doing?"

"It's turned off, and I'm turned on."

She laughed. "I'm not playing second fiddle to an alarm clock. Besides, I'll be late."

He slipped in beside her and started nibbling

176

on her neck. "I called in for you. We're taking the day off," he murmured.

"You what!"

"I'm taking you out to a nice, leisurely breakfast; then we have an appointment with your doctor. I want to be as informed a father as I can be. But first . . ." His lips and hands moved lower.

Rachel started to object, but Zachary's touch was awakening both her and her desire. She would object later.

And object she did. Not to breakfast, which was delicious and filling. Nor to the pleasant task of educating Zachary to her condition and what he could do to make the pregnancy easier for her. She did, however, object quite strongly when they went for the marriage license.

Zachary was very patient and convincing. "Rachel, honey, it's just a formality. And there's no rush. It's good for a month or so, and if we haven't decided on a date by then, we can get another."

She finally agreed, looking relieved by his arguments. He just smiled enigmatically.

Later that evening Zachary received a mysterious phone call, then told her he had to go to Dallas right away but would be back tomorrow. They made a date for the next evening. He kissed her and dashed off, leaving her at her apartment with an uneasy feeling something was going on behind her back. It was a feeling that increased the next day.

Rachel didn't know what was going on around her business, but she intended to find out. All her employees were walking around with big smiles, and it was driving her crazy. She knew who was probably responsible for everyone grinning at her. "Zachary Lyons, please," she said impatiently after reaching his office by phone. "This is Rachel Jordan calling."

"He just got back. I'll put you straight through," his secretary informed her efficiently.

"Hello, sweet Rachel." Zachary's voice rang out. "And just why do I have the pleasure of hearing your voice in the middle of the day? You're all right, aren't you?" he asked on a more serious note.

"I'm fine, Zachary," she told him. "You wouldn't happen to know why my staff is going around all smiles today, I suppose."

"Now how would I know that?" he replied teasingly.

"Zachary Lyons, just what have you been up to? You didn't tell them I was pregnant, did you?" she accused.

"Rachel, I'm shocked. Just what kind of man do you think I am? I don't plant my seed and tell. Really, I'm hurt," he said in an affronted tone, but Rachel could hear the laughter in his voice, loud and clear.

"Did you?" she repeated.

"No, of course I didn't," he replied indignantly.

"I know something's up, Zachary, and I know you're in on it."

"I can't imagine what it could be, Rachel," he stated innocently. "Perhaps you should talk to Martin?"

"I already did. He called me paranoid, but I know better. He's so closemouthed air wouldn't escape if he didn't want it to."

"Angela?"

"Yes, and all she'll tell me is there's a new man in her life," Rachel told him dryly.

"Must be one heck of a guy if she can't erase her smile. Maybe I should take some pointers."

"You don't need any, Zachary, and I didn't call to stroke your already big ego. I'll say goodbye."

"Wait, Rachel! You aren't going to forget our date tonight, are you?" he asked hurriedly.

"Zachary, I forget only one date," she informed him frostily.

"Well, you never know about pregnant ladies. They get funny ideas, like everyone's smiling at them, and they certainly can get grouchy."

"Can I send a stranglegram?"

"A what?"

"You know. Like flowers or a singing telegram? I'd like to send someone over there to strangle you."

"Now, Rachel, don't get upset. It's not good for the baby. I just have special plans for this evening, and I was reminding you, that's all," he told her in a soothingly calm voice.

179

"What plans?" she asked suspiciously.

"It's a surprise. You'll have to remember our date if you want to find out."

"Surprises aren't good for the baby either, Zachary. Couldn't you just give me a hint?" She coaxed him sweetly.

"No. Then it wouldn't be a complete surprise," he said, finality in his voice.

"You're no fun."

"I will be later. We'll see just how much fun you can stand, sweet Rachel."

"Good-bye, Zachary," she said firmly.

"See you at seven, Rachel."

She didn't know what he was up to, but she was sure she wouldn't like it. At that moment her phone started ringing, and she lost track of time; but her suspicions returned later when Angela called.

"Rachel, there's a package over here for you. Do you want me to sign for it?" Angela asked.

Perhaps this would provide a clue to Zachary's surprise. "Yes. And bring it right over, Angela, please." She hadn't ordered anything through the mail. She could barely contain her curiosity until Angela arrived with the package.

"What do you think it is, Rachel?" Angela asked as she came into the office with a small box. "It came by special messenger, and the guy said not to let it get too hot."

"I won't know till I open it, now will I?"

"Well, hurry up. You know I can't stand suspense!"

"You must be terrible at Christmas. I bet you peek into all your presents early." Rachel shook the box. "I wonder what it is?"

"Rachel!"

"Okay, okay. I'm opening it. See?" she asked as she peeled off the paper. "I'm glad you didn't handle it for long if it's not supposed to get hot."

"What do you mean by that?"

"After what you told me about the new man in your life? I'm afraid your thoughts alone could melt whatever's in here."

"Hah! What about you and Zachary? Talk about hot!" she responded quickly, rolling her eyes heavenward. "Come on, come on!" she cried, nearly pushing Rachel aside to look into the box. "Oh, Rachel!"

"Yes, oh yes!" she agreed, staring at the carved antique car. She took it out of the box. "It's made of milk chocolate! Must weigh a couple of pounds," she exclaimed gleefully. "And it's mine, all mine."

"You could at least let me have a small bite, Rachel. Think of all those calories," Angela said coaxingly, almost drooling at the sight of the chocolate, just waiting to be eaten. "How about that fender there?"

"First I'll have to show it to everyone. Martin will want to take a picture of it, I'm sure."

"Just don't forget me when you start eating it," Angela said as she went back to work.

Rachel set the chocolate down and picked up the small envelope in the bottom of the box. The handwriting was Zachary's. "Sweets for the sweet, how horny can I get." The usual outrageous Zachary. She read the second line. "Seriously, Rachel, I'm really not up on the cravings of pregnant ladies, but I thought you and the baby would enjoy this. Love, Zachary."

"Dear Zachary," she said out loud, "how you make me laugh and feel so special." Tears came to her eyes at the thought of his eccentricities and how they touched her. The phone rang again, and it was back to business and back to earth. If she didn't get busy, she was going to be late for her date!

"Come on, Zachary, at least give me a little hint," Rachel said coaxingly as they left her place later that evening.

"Not one. You'll just have to wait," he answered.

Rachel knew by the look on his face he wouldn't change his mind. "Oh, all right." She thanked him for the chocolate and told him if she didn't like his surprise, he couldn't have any. But he didn't appear worried, so she sat back to enjoy the drive. When they pulled into his driveway, she could barely tolerate the suspense.

"Go on in, honey, I'm right behind you," Zachary said.

"Well, hurry up," she called over her shoulder as she unlocked the front door and walked into the living room. Her mother, Sarah Jordan, welcomed her. "Mother!" Rachel cried in disbelief, almost unaware of the woman sitting beside her.

Zachary came in behind her. "Rachel, this is Jane Lyons, my mother."

Rachel's mind was running fast. What were they both doing here? "What a surprise," she said uncertainly.

"Rachel, you know I wouldn't miss your wedding."

"Nor would I," Jane said. "We're both so pleased."

"Wedding?" Rachel asked, going pale.

"Rachel, honey, are you all right?" both of the older women chimed at once.

"Yes, I'm fine. It's been a long day, that's all," she replied, sitting down. *And it's going to be an even longer night when I get you alone, Zachary*, Rachel thought as she looked at him, her eyes shooting daggers. He simply smiled at her innocently.

"Your wedding dress is just gorgeous," Sarah said.

Rachel looked away from Zachary, realizing her mother was talking to her. "It is? I mean, yes, isn't it? Just perfect." What wedding dress? She looked back at Zachary. *Don't look so smug, buster, just wait.*

"I want you to know how pleased I am about the wedding, Rachel," Zachary's mother said.

Again Rachel realized she was being spoken to. She had really better concentrate on this conversation and deal with him later.

It was a long evening. Rachel thought she would never get him alone. But finally the ladies excused themselves and went off to bed. Now she had him. "I'm waiting."

"For what?"

"Do you realize I don't even know where or when we're getting married?" she stated sarcastically. "And that I had to be told what my own wedding dress looks like?" She continued heatedly. "This was a rotten stunt to pull, and you know it!"

"If you don't want to get married, just tell our mothers," Zachary said calmly.

"After you so generously allowed *me* to tell them their first grandchild is on the way?" she asked incredulously.

"Well, it will still be their grandchild."

"Oh, Zachary, what am I going to do with you? I suppose next you'll be dashing into the delivery room and telling the doctor how to deliver the baby," she said, exasperated.

"Actually I have been reading up on it and—"

"Will you be serious? I'm trying to be mad at you."

Zachary came over to where she stood, arms folded across her chest. "I hope, openly and of your own free will, that you are going to marry me this Saturday. I love you, Rachel. I want to take care of you and have you take care of me, to love me, have my children and be with me to the end of our lives and beyond. I need you, and you need me. Will you marry me and be my love, Rachel?" he asked.

She sighed and unfolded her arms, smiling through tears of happiness. "Yes," she replied. "I will, and I do love you." She knew she had finally accepted the complete love he had for her and she for him.

"Is she okay?" Rachel asked as Zachary came back into their bedroom.

"Yes, she's fine," he said, his eyes lighting up at the sight of Rachel sitting up in bed, her nightgown barely covering her curves. "I informed Sarah Jane she's not to disturb us until morning."

"And do you think she'll mind you?" Rachel asked, laughing at the thought of their two-month-old daughter obeying Zachary's orders.

"I hope so. It's time she learned I have more claims on her mother than she does," he said, sitting down beside her on the bed.

"Zachary, you don't fool me. One squeak, and you'll be in there in a flash," she said teasingly.

"Well, something could be wrong," Zachary said defensively. His eyes softened at the mention of his daughter.

"You're going to spoil her rotten if you aren't careful. She needs to cry sometimes. She can't always have her own way."

"Okay. So you let her cry when I'm not here."

"Zachary . . ." Rachel warned.

"All right, I'll try. I promise," he said, rolling

his eyes. "Cross my heart. Right now, though, I'd rather play with you," he said wickedly. "I got a call from Dr. Morgan today. Did she tell you also?" he continued mischievously, his hands brushing her shoulders to let the straps of her nightgown fall.

"Tell me what?" she asked innocently.

"I think I'd rather show you," he said, his whole face showing sheer delight as the night-gown slid to her waist. "I think it's a good idea if we try for a few more babies anyway. We wouldn't want Sarah Jane too spoiled by her mommy, now would we?" he said teasingly, giving in to the temptation to touch her. "Such beautiful, full breasts," he mumbled, smothering his face between them.

"Me spoil her!" she exclaimed. Then the full implications of what he had said hit her. "Zachary? What if I don't get pregnant again?"

"Then we'll still have fun trying," he replied, caressing her breasts.

"Zachary, I'm serious."

"Rachel," he said, pulling her into his arms, holding her tightly, "we've been blessed with one healthy, beautiful baby girl. If that's all there is, then we accept her as the miracle she is. And I'm positive you can keep me from spoiling her too much," he added, stroking her hair. "But we're sure going to give it one hell of a try. I've been restraining myself for months for you, and I hope you're ready for me," he growled in her ear, a twinkle in his eyes as she pulled back to look at him.

"I think you'll just have to find that out for yourself." She ran her fingers across his flat stomach.

"I've really missed you, love," he said, discovering her body all over again.

"I haven't been anywhere," she replied, wanting to touch him everywhere at once.

"Neither have I, for months, and I'm not sure I can find home again," Zachary whispered.

"Then I'll have to guide you, love," Rachel returned sensually. Loving the feel of his hands on her, she knew now, no matter what happened, more babies or not, what she already had was more than enough. She was loved and she loved in return, without reservation.

All-new

Candlelight Newsletter

**An exceptional,
free offer awaits readers
of Dell's incomparable Candlelight Ecstasy and Supreme Romances.**

Subscribe to our all-new CANDLELIGHT NEWSLETTER and you will receive—at absolutely no cost to you—exciting, exclusive information about today's finest romance novels and novelists. You'll be part of a select group to receive sneak previews of upcoming Candlelight Romances, well in advance of publication.

You'll also go behind the scenes to "meet" our Ecstasy and Supreme authors, learning firsthand where they get their ideas and how they made it to the top. News of author appearances and events will be detailed, as well. And contributions from the Candlelight editor will give you the inside scoop on how she makes her decisions about what to publish—and how *you* can try your hand at writing an Ecstasy or Supreme.

You'll find all this and more in Dell's CANDLELIGHT NEWSLETTER. And best of all, *it costs you nothing*. That's right! It's Dell's way of thanking our loyal Candlelight readers and of adding another dimension to your reading enjoyment.

Just fill out the coupon below, return it to us, and look forward to receiving the first of many CANDLELIGHT NEWSLETTERS—overflowing with the kind of excitement that only enhances our romances!

B252A

Return to: DELL PUBLISHING CO., INC.
        Candlelight Newsletter • Publicity Department
        245 East 47 Street • New York, N.Y. 10017

Name_____

Address_____

City_____

State_____ Zip_____

Candlelight Ecstasy Romances™

$1.95 each

At your local bookstore or use this handy coupon for ordering:

DELL BOOKS
P.O. BOX 1000, PINE BROOK, N.J. 07058-1000   B252B

Please send me the books I have checked above. I am enclosing $ _____ (please add 75c per copy to cover postage and handling). Send check or money order—no cash or C.O.D.'s. Please allow up to 8 weeks for shipment.

Name _____

Address _____

City _____ State / Zip _____

Candlelight
Ecstasy Romances™